STATE SMART!

Over 130 Ready-to-Use Puzzle Activities Based on the Geography & History of the 50 United States

JOHN H. THOMPSON

THE CENTER FOR APPLIED RESEARCH IN EDUCATION
West Nyack, New York 10994

Many of the illustrations in this resource are reproductions from the Dover Clip-Art Series® and the fine Dover Pictorial Archive Series.

10 9 8 7 6 5 4 3 2 1

Library of Congress Cataloging-in-Publication Data

Thompson, John H.
State smart! : over 130 ready-to-use puzzle activities based on the geography & history of the 50 United States / John H. Thompson.
p. cm.
ISBN 0-87628-881-6
1. Geographical recreations—United States. 2. Puzzles.
I. Title.
GV148.T56 1995
793.73—dc20 95-6468
CIP

The Center for Applied Research in Education, Professional Publishing
West Nyack, NY 10994
A Simon & Schuster Company

Printed in the United States of America

About This Resource

The purpose of this resource is to help you meet one of the many daily challenges that face any teacher today—the ability to create lessons that are informative, interesting, and exciting for your students, but not time-consuming for you to prepare. Puzzle activities based on geography and history are a unique way to stimulate students' interest in the states and regions of our country. You will find that students enjoy learning a variety of unusual facts about the United States of America.

Specifically, the goals of *STATE SMART!* are

- to save the instructor valuable time in lesson preparation,
- to provide information and ideas that challenge all students,
- to provide students with an opportunity for independent thinking and research while completing directed activities,
- to enliven geography and history lessons with activities that are enjoyable and meaningful for students,
- to encourage correct spelling and vocabulary mastery,
- to provide appropriate review activities or enrichment exercises,
- to provide students with structured activities that can be successfully used in a cooperative learning situation.

With this collection of ready-to-use puzzle activities, you can spark involvement in students of varying abilities while shortening your lesson planning and preparation time by hours.

Included in this resource are numerous reproducible activities appropriate for students in grades five through twelve. The puzzles cover various information about all of the United States, for example: the original thirteen states, the New England states, the Middle Atlantic states, the southern states, the midwestern states, the Rocky Mountain states, and the Pacific Coast states. Other puzzles include such unique topics as state nicknames, state mottoes, state flowers, and state historical highlights. Students especially enjoy researching the trivia clues in the puzzles about state oddities and specialties, state places to visit, and famous sons and daughters. To help you guide your students' research, I have included a list of state agencies from which students can find information to solve the puzzles as well as other useful material that can further stimulate their interest in the diverse geography and history of our country.

For quick and easy access, the puzzles are listed by region or topic. Each puzzle is ready to be photocopied as many times as necessary for use with individual students, small groups, or the entire class. Complete answer keys are provided at the end of the book and may also be photocopied or placed at a central location if you wish students to correct their own work.

The activities in this resource have many possible uses, for example, homework assignments, extra-credit activities, make-up tests, emergency or daily lesson plans, textbook reviews, or individual workbooks. The puzzles may also be used as enrichment activities in a learning center setting, where students choose the activities that appeal to them and can work individually or with others to solve them. Few students can resist the challenge of solving puzzles; puzzles motivate unexcited and less capable students and provide excellent reinforcement for highly motivated students who finish assignments ahead of others. In addition, you can use the puzzles to break a dull daily routine.

I have found that the most productive uses of these activities are to arouse students' interest at the beginning of a lesson, to serve as a steppingstone for a class discussion, and to review information at the end of a lesson. Geographical and historical facts take on new life and meaning when they become part of a puzzle!

John H. Thompson

About the Author

John H. Thompson received his B.A. in English and History from East Tennessee State University in Johnson City. He has been a teacher in the public schools of Tennessee, Arizona, and Virginia for over twenty years and has taught English, American government, economics, geography, international relations, world history, and United States history. His students have been diverse also, ranging in level from eighth-grade remedial students to adults, and coming from many ethnic groups. He is a member of the National Council for the Social Studies and Virginia Council for the Social Studies.

Mr. Thompson is also the author of *HOOKED ON AMERICAN HISTORY!* published in 1993 by The Center for Applied Research in Education, and *HOOKED ON PRESIDENTS!* published in 1995, also by The Center.

Contents

Individual State Puzzles

Name ______________________ Date ______________

1. THE ORIGINAL THIRTEEN STATES—I

ACROSS:

1. State originally claimed by the Swedes
3. State with the first constitution
6. State that was originally part of New York
7. State that had the first college, Harvard
8. State originally claimed by the Quakers
10. State originally claimed by the Dutch
13. Major producer of tobacco

DOWN:

2. Smallest of the original thirteen states
4. Northernmost of the original thirteen states
5. State with the most slaves
9. First of the original thirteen states to be settled, in 1607
11. State originally claimed by the Catholics
12. Southernmost of the original thirteen states

2. THE ORIGINAL THIRTEEN STATES—II

ACROSS: ____

1. River by which the nation's capital was built
2. Native American who married Virginia settler John Rolfe
3. State that was originally part of New York
4. Leader of a rebellion of poor farmers in Virginia in 1676
5. Major seaport in the southern states
6. Home state of the first president of the United States
7. Native American tribe in Rhode Island
8. Founder of Rhode Island
9. New York capital, originally named Fort Orange
10. Second smallest of the original states
11. State that donated the land for the nation's capital
12. Religious sect that settled in Maryland
13. Leader of a rebellion of poor farmers in Massachusetts in 1786
14. Maryland city named after its founder
15. Connecticut capital, originally named Fort Good Hope
16. Original settlers of New York
17. Original settlers of Delaware
18. Religious sect that settled in Pennsylvania
19. River that separates Georgia and South Carolina
20. State originally settled by the Pilgrims
21. First permanent English settlement in America
22. Mountain range that formed the western boundary of the original states
23. First permanent English settlement in Massachusetts
24. River that separates New Hampshire and Vermont
25. Smallest of the original states

Name ______________________________ Date ____________________

2. The Original Thirteen States—II

1 _ _ T _ _ _ _
2 _ _ _ _ H _ _ _ _ _
3 _ _ _ _ E _ _ _ _

4 _ _ _ O _
5 _ _ _ R _ _ _ _ _ _
6 _ _ _ _ I _ _ _
7 _ _ _ _ _ G _ _ _ _ _ _
8 _ _ _ _ I _ _ _
9 _ _ _ _ N _
10 _ _ _ A _ _ _ _
11 _ _ _ _ L _ _ _

12 _ _ T _ _ _ _ _ _
13 _ H _ _ _
14 _ _ _ _ I _ _ _ _
15 _ _ R _ _ _ _ _
16 _ _ T _ _
17 _ _ E _ _ _
18 _ _ _ _ E _ _
19 _ _ _ _ N _ _ _

20 _ _ _ S _ _ _ _ _ _ _ _ _
21 _ _ _ _ _ T _ _ _
22 _ _ _ _ _ A _ _ _ _ _ _
23 _ _ _ _ _ _ T _
24 _ _ _ _ E _ _ _ _ _ _
25 _ _ _ _ _ _ S _ _ _ _

3. THE ORIGINAL THIRTEEN STATES—III

The answers to the following clues are hidden in the puzzle. Circle the answer in the puzzle and then write the answer in the blank by the correct number. Answers can be found horizontally, vertically, diagonally, and backward.

1. "Father of the Constitution" and author of the Bill of Rights
2. River that separates Virginia and Maryland
3. Second smallest of the original thirteen states
4. State in which American troops camped at Valley Forge during the bitter winter of 1777–78
5. Nickname of Connecticut
6. Capital city of Virginia
7. River that separates South Carolina and Georgia
8. Capital city of Georgia
9. Nickname of New York
10. A major crop of Virginia, Maryland, and North Carolina
11. Capital city of South Carolina
12. State that donated the land for the nation's capital
13. Nickname of Delaware
14. State where the American Revolution began
15. Chairman of the Constitutional Convention and first president
16. Capital city of Rhode Island
17. Nickname of North Carolina
18. Capital city of Delaware
19. Author of the Declaration of Independence
20. Northernmost state of the original thirteen states
21. Capital city of Pennsylvania
22. Nickname of Georgia
23. First of the original thirteen states to sign the Constitution
24. State where the Americans won their first victory in the Revolutionary War
25. Nickname of Virginia
26. Capital city of North Carolina
27. Chairman of the Second Continental Congress, who stated, "I shall sign so boldly the king shall read it without his glasses."
28. City where the Declaration of Independence and the Constitution were signed
29. Nickname of Maryland
30. Region of rolling hills in the southern states at the base of the Appalachians
31. Capital city of New York
32. State where the American Revolution ended
33. Nickname of Pennsylvania
34. Capital city of Connecticut
35. Delegate to the Second Continental Congress, who stated, "We must all hang together or most assuredly we shall all hang separately."
36. Capital city of New Jersey
37. Nickname of Massachusetts
38. The first vice president of the United States
39. Mountains that formed the western boundary of the original thirteen states
40. Nickname of Rhode Island
41. Capital city of New Hampshire
42. Southernmost state of the original thirteen states
43. Nickname of New Hampshire
44. A major southern seaport in the original thirteen states
45. Flat coastal plain in the southern states, with land so low in places that the rivers crossing it flow backward with the incoming tides
46. Capital city of Massachusetts
47. River that separates Pennsylvania and New Jersey
48. Smallest of the original thirteen states
49. Nickname of New Jersey
50. Capital city of Maryland

Name ______________________ Date ______________

3. The Original Thirteen States-III

```
B A R E T A T S Y A B C O N R A L E I G H F G H T
G E M A R Y L A N D O V E R A M R Y L C A R S R E
G E O R G A E T A T S E T I N A R G O B U T E V E
M T O H A S W A S H I N H O W A A N T B O N S O N
T A D R A L B A N Y I P E A X P S R S Y T S U O L
A T B C G R Z O L I L Q L A P T E I E O F C T J D
K S E A L E M O R E S E T A I T R S N U A S C O F
G H N M H J W M D O D R L T A R R A A A E S V H N
T C J O O C C A B O T A U W A E T I Y L W E T N K
X A A T S Y L A S A C T E H J A G N R B R Z N C B
C E M O D I E G T H I D E W R R H A I A K O O E P
R P I P H S D N I O I C E H O T H V X N B C M M D
M A N P R Y A A N T N N E E H C A L D Y N A D P L
I O F T I L N S M E T E G S F L T Y E A H E E I C
W C R A T S T S D S L W H T I H T S H E G R I R A
S E A A S A N I M S E R E V O D O N X E I H P E V
E A N R T Y V W T A H M E M E N H N D H E O R S E
T N K E H O A A I T S T A N M O A E S G L D R T Y
W S L E R N T N T A A S O J J T L P H A A E E A L
S T I P A E I M V T J I A O B A M W I R R I A T S
I A N S U G R A S E N E H C W A T B O D G S O E I
L T I F R O N R F I L N N A H L M O W E E L D D H
O E E I R N E F M T A O R W O U S C H N O A O R L
P O V N A K E O E D T E E D L A S Y W S H N I O C
A H W H A R D A A S S N E O A G A E I T N D S C T
N T H U S D E M O R U L C F R E E S T A T E E N S
N X Q O L S S B U M B T I C H D R O F T R A H O F
A D N O M H C I R Y F I R S T S T A T E S A C C K
```

1. ______
2. ______
3. ______
4. ______
5. ______
6. ______
7. ______
8. ______
9. ______
10. ______
11. ______
12. ______
13. ______
14. ______
15. ______
16. ______
17. ______
18. ______
19. ______
20. ______
21. ______
22. ______
23. ______
24. ______
25. ______
26. ______
27. ______
28. ______
29. ______
30. ______
31. ______
32. ______
33. ______
34. ______
35. ______
36. ______
37. ______
38. ______
39. ______
40. ______
41. ______
42. ______
43. ______
44. ______
45. ______
46. ______
47. ______
48. ______
49. ______
50. ______

4. THE LOUISIANA PURCHASE

ACROSS:

1. River in the central portion of the Louisiana Territory
2. Explorer of the northern portion of the Louisiana Territory
3. U.S. president who purchased the Louisiana Territory in 1803
4. Explorer of the southern portion of the Louisiana Territory
5. River in the northern portion of the Louisiana Territory
6. City from which Lewis and Clark left on their expedition through the Louisiana Territory
7. American ambassador who helped arrange the Louisiana Purchase
8. River that formed the eastern boundary of the Louisiana Territory
9. Explorer of the northern portion of the Louisiana Territory
10. European explorer who named the Louisiana Territory
11. River in the southern portion of the Louisiana Territory
12. Native American woman who served as an interpreter and guide for Lewis and Clark
13. French dictator who sold the Louisiana Territory to the United States
14. River that Lewis and Clark followed on their expedition through the Louisiana Territory
15. Slave who helped Lewis and Clark explore the Louisiana Territory
16. Mountains that formed the western boundary of the Louisiana Territory
17. Native American tribe that helped Lewis and Clark on their expedition through the Louisiana Territory
18. European country that sold the Louisiana Territory to the United States
19. American ambassador who helped arrange the Louisiana Purchase
20. Port at the mouth of the Mississippi River

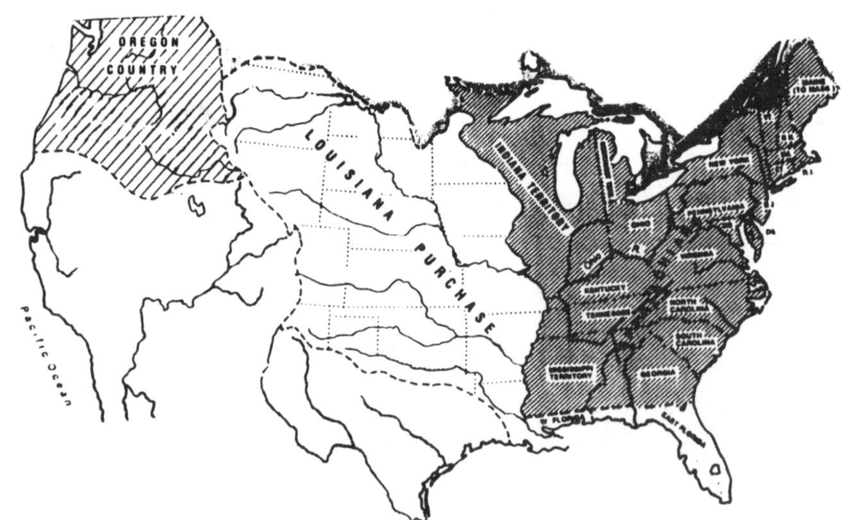

Name ______________________________ Date ____________________

4. The Louisiana Purchase

1 T
2 H
3 E

4 L
5 O
6 U
7 I
8 S
9 I
10 A
11 N
12 A

13 P
14 U
15 R
16 C
17 H
18 A
19 S
20 E

5. THE WESTERN FRONTIER

The answers to the following clues are hidden in the puzzle. Circle the answer in the puzzle and then write the answer in the blank by the correct number. Answers can be found horizontally, vertically, diagonally, and backward.

1. Self-appointed law enforcers who tracked down outlaws in the West
2. The first territory to grant women the right to vote, in 1869, before any of the states east of the Mississippi River
3. Vehicle used to carry food and supplies on long cattle drives
4. Name used on early maps for the area west of the Mississippi River, due to the lack of trees and inadequate rainfall
5. Immigrant laborers who did much of the backbreaking work in constructing the first railroad through the Sierra Nevada
6. Site of a massacre of Native Americans in Colorado in 1864
7. Leader of the Nez Percé, who surrendered near the Canadian border in 1877
8. Route for driving cattle from Texas to Kansas
9. Apache chief who surrendered in Arizona in 1886
10. Nickname of the large, cloth-covered wagons used by the western pioneers
11. Trapper and frontiersman known as the "Daniel Boone of the Rocky Mountains"
12. Slogan for western expansion
13. Communities left behind by western settlers after gold or silver strikes had been played out
14. African American mountain man who was accepted as a chief among the Crow Indians
15. Religious leader who moved his followers to the Great Salt Lake area of Utah
16. U.S. Army captain who became famous for his explorations of the Sierra Nevada, "the Pathfinder"
17. Wild Texas cattle
18. One of the best-known African American cowboys, "Deadwood Dick"
19. African Americans who moved from the post-Reconstruction South to Kansas
20. First of the popular western cow towns in Kansas
21. Western outlaw Henry McCarty, who committed his first murder at the age of thirteen
22. Oklahoma settlers who jumped the gun on claiming free western homesteads
23. Postal system by which mail was relayed from Missouri to California on swift horses
24. Western drifter who was shot while playing poker, the cards he was holding now referred to as the "dead-man's hand"
25. House on the Great Plains, made of strips of turf because trees and stones were so scarce
26. Inventor of barbed wire in 1874, putting an end to the open range
27. Nickname of California gold rushers
28. U.S. military commander who was killed with all his men at the Battle of the Little Bighorn in 1876
29. Animal that provided subsistence for the Native Americans of the Great Plains
30. Sacred area of the Sioux Indians, Paha Sapa
31. Native American commander, Tashunka Witko, who defeated the U.S. Army in the last and greatest Indian victory
32. Site of a massacre of Native Americans in South Dakota in 1890
33. Nickname of Martha Canary, a mule skinner, scout, and friend of famous western outlaws
34. Native American medicine man who succeeded in forming an alliance between the Arapaho, Cheyenne, and Sioux in 1876
35. Nickname of William F. Cody, owner of a touring Wild West show
36. Site of an American battle with Mexicans in 1836
37. Route from Missouri to the Pacific Northwest
38. Man who discovered gold in California in 1848 on the property of Johann Sutter
39. Symbol on the California flag
40. Settler who led American families to Texas in 1823
41. Territory bought from Mexico in 1853 to provide a path for a transcontinental railroad through the Southwest
42. Fort built to protect settlers traveling on the Oregon Trail
43. President of the independent Republic of Texas, elected in 1836
44. River separating Texas and Mexico
45. Route from Missouri to New Mexico
46. Religious sect that settled in Utah in 1847
47. Large wagon covered with sailcloth and pulled by oxen
48. Folk hero killed at the Alamo
49. U.S. president when Oregon, New Mexico, and California were annexed by the United States
50. Symbol on the Texas flag

Name ______________________________ Date ____________________

5. The Western Frontier

```
L T B R I G H A M Y O U N G W E S A C P W A F
L R A E B Y L Z Z I R G E E N K D E D N U O W
I D P O N Y E X P R E S S K L O P K S E M A J
B E I E N A J Y T I M A L A C S N O M R O M C
O E D N A R G O I R B I L L Y T H E K I D A A
L C O N E S T O G A A S L A K A B I L E N E W
A L O L A F F U B R A A N O G A W K C U H C P
F O A C C R C N T M H I K E N M O R M O N S L
F N T R A T G E H S C C H I N E S E B C R V I
U G A R F T F O R H I P T M X A L U H E D K A
B H R Y E A U A I H R S K A J C F I N J E G R
S O P E T S M M L R U O S R R F S O A E S C T
I R M N T S E L A A C D G A A H O M R R R N N
T N A O E S I D N N G D Z L O H E C E P E H O
T S N M E B U E N H I Y O L C S D N Y D N R G
I O A A D W H C O A H F M S B N I T D S O E E
N J T L G P Y S E O C T E E A N F I D E O G R
G P I A E B T O R G R I C S Y H L N O T S D O
B W B T R T F S M A R K R T T G O T S N H I B
U M S T O F E A I I W O R E H D N W C A S R L
L J P W N M F L A O N O E P M M E N E L I B A
L P N K I L S R U R F G E G B A S S D I L M C
F S A H M H P R R A T S E N O L T B T G S I K
C L E V O L T A N G O M A L A K A A M I D J H
J L F D C H I E F J O S E P H J R J E V N F I
N O T S U O H M A S R E T S U D O X E R M Y L
Y M C S C M E S A H C R U P N E D S D A G R L
L D A V Y C R O C K E T T H W E I M A R A L S
H T M S B A T N O M E R F N H O J E R O P T E
```

1. ____________________
2. ____________________
3. ____________________
4. ____________________
5. ____________________
6. ____________________
7. ____________________
8. ____________________
9. ____________________
10. ____________________
11. ____________________
12. ____________________
13. ____________________
14. ____________________
15. ____________________
16. ____________________
17. ____________________
18. ____________________
19. ____________________
20. ____________________
21. ____________________
22. ____________________
23. ____________________
24. ____________________
25. ____________________
26. ____________________
27. ____________________
28. ____________________
29. ____________________
30. ____________________
31. ____________________
32. ____________________
33. ____________________
34. ____________________
35. ____________________
36. ____________________
37. ____________________
38. ____________________
39. ____________________
40. ____________________
41. ____________________
42. ____________________
43. ____________________
44. ____________________
45. ____________________
46. ____________________
47. ____________________
48. ____________________
49. ____________________
50. ____________________

6. THE CIVIL WAR—STATES OF THE UNION

ACROSS: ___

4. Location of the battle of Antietam
5. Location of the Union prisoner-of-war camp called Camp Douglas
7. Slave state remaining in the Union
9. Another slave state remaining in the Union
14. Home state of the Fifty-fourth Regiment of African American volunteers
17. President Lincoln's state of residence
18. Location of the U.S. Military Academy
19. Birthplace of President Lincoln
20. Home state of Union general Ulysses S. Grant

DOWN: ___

1. State that supplied food for the Union
2. Another slave state remaining in the Union
3. Location of the battle of Gettysburg
6. Another state that supplied food for the Union
8. Smallest state in the Union
10. "Bleeding ___________"
11. State that seceded from Virginia and remained in the Union
12. State that supplied gold for the Union
13. Home state of William McKinley, the last Civil War veteran to rise to the presidency
15. Location of a riot against the drafting of Union soldiers in 1863, in which more than seventy-five people were killed
16. State where President Lincoln is buried

Name ______________________ Date ______________

6. The Civil War—States of the Union

7. THE CIVIL WAR—STATES OF THE CONFEDERACY

ACROSS:

4. Home state of Confederate general Robert E. Lee
5. Largest of the Confederate states
9. State in which the Confederate prisoner-of-war camp at Andersonville was located
11. Last southern state to secede from the Union
12. Slave state that seceded after the battle of Fort Sumter
15. Namesake of a Confederate ship built in Great Britain
16. Location of General Sherman's "March to the Sea"
17. Home state of Confederate President Jefferson Davis
18. Location of the battles of Chancellorsville and Fredericksburg
19. Slave state that seceded after the battle of Fort Sumter

DOWN:

1. Location of the first and second battles of Bull Run
2. Location of the Monitor–Merrimac battle
3. First state that seceded from the Union
5. Location of the battles of Fort Henry and Fort Donelson
6. Namesake of another Confederate ship built in Great Britain
7. Location of the battle of Shiloh
8. Location of the battle of Vicksburg
10. Location of the battle of Chickamauga
13. Location of the battles of Port Hudson and New Orleans
14. State in which the Confederate capital, Richmond, was located
15. Namesake of the first cruiser constructed abroad for the Confederate navy, launched at Liverpool, England, in 1862

Name ______________________ Date ______________________

7. The Civil War—States of the Confederacy

8. THE CIVIL WAR

The answers to the following clues are hidden in the puzzle. Circle the answer in the puzzle and then write the answer in the blank by the correct number. Answers can be found horizontally, vertically, diagonally, and backward.

1. Location of the first battle of the Civil War
2. Nickname of the Confederate flag
3. President of the Confederate States of America
4. President of the United States of America
5. First state to secede from the Union
6. Last state to secede from the Union
7. Union commander at Fort Sumter
8. Original Confederate capital
9. Location of two battles during the Civil War
10. Bloodiest battle of the Civil War
11. Commander of the Confederate troops
12. Commander of the Union troops
13. Nickname of Confederate commander Thomas Jackson
14. Nickname for paper money issued by the Union
15. Union ironclad ship
16. Confederate ironclad ship
17. Union commander who stated, "Damn the torpedoes, full steam ahead"
18. Union commander who stated, "War is hell"
19. Author of "The Battle Hymn of the Republic"
20. Superintendent of Union nurses
21. Union nurse who later founded the American Red Cross
22. Female Confederate spy
23. Female Union spy
24. Union commander from whose name "sideburns" became a term for long whiskers
25. Battle in which a famous Confederate general was unintentionally killed by his own troops
26. Important Civil War battle, called the "high water mark of the Confederacy"
27. Location of the Confederate surrender
28. Confederate warship built in Great Britain
29. President Lincoln's decision to free the slaves
30. Confederate prisoner-of-war camp in Georgia
31. Confederate commander who led a daring charge at the battle of Gettysburg
32. Nickname of Union commander Ulysses S. Grant
33. Confederate capital
34. Decisive battle that gave the Union forces control of the Mississippi River
35. Union commander known as "Tardy George"
36. Location of a bloody Civil War battle in Tennessee
37. Another Confederate warship built in Great Britain
38. Confederate city destroyed during General Sherman's "March to the Sea"
39. Confederate prison camp commander who was executed as a war criminal in 1864
40. Nickname given to northerners who opposed the war; after a poisonous snake

Name ______________________________ Date ____________________

8. The Civil War

```
D Y R K J H G P S C M C G P H O T T H J F P C B H
N B T C F M S D A E H R E P P O C F P J T L H G E
M E M L C K P S B A R D L F A H M Y H S A C G D L
K M D A N D E R S O N V I L L E R J D R J L I C S
C M J D L S W I L L I A M S H E R M A N M S Y H R
R L M A O P R C A M I R R E M C D B M C N M J E A
C W E V C J E A R I C H M O N D A B C R A W H N S
D O H I N S C F B W S A G N U R L L U B W C I R N
J H J D I T R A K D D T B J T L E B S D T L L Y E
A N R F L O M D M O N I T O R L E I A U O G L W S
W E E A M N A I E O O A N T L S V M B R R R A I J
O E H R A E T R M N M S S A O A A E A U E T U R M
N R R R H W E O T O D M N R D B H C B T L M A Z Y
K G I A A A I L L P E A B N A T H S M A T R P I C
K E B G R L T F E J H M O L E T K U N S U T P T C
H S B U B L N I U T A S A N U C S T S K S N O E E
N O I T A M A L C O R P N O I T A P I C N A M E R
O R Y L O H I W A E A E S V R E R I C A H R A A R
D H O N O A E T F Y S C B O U T T D A B R G T N E
L L H L H J N F O S H N F O S O N D E N F S T A R
M E I O R A E W E I R O B E R T A N D E R S O N L
L H W I L J E E J O S E N O G A L E S E M E X A R
S E T T Y I S I X I D A E H T O R O D R P S E R O
B M A R K E H T T E K C I P E G R O E G L S L A C
T H G E T T Y S B U R G W A N A T H W B T Y S T H
S W X Y Z A B C C H A N C E L L O R S V I L L E W
G N F R S I O N S B H B G F Y A S I O H A U W I O
```

1. ____________________
2. ____________________
3. ____________________
4. ____________________
5. ____________________
6. ____________________
7. ____________________
8. ____________________
9. ____________________
10. ____________________
11. ____________________
12. ____________________
13. ____________________
14. ____________________
15. ____________________
16. ____________________
17. ____________________
18. ____________________
19. ____________________
20. ____________________
21. ____________________
22. ____________________
23. ____________________
24. ____________________
25. ____________________
26. ____________________
27. ____________________
28. ____________________
29. ____________________
30. ____________________
31. ____________________
32. ____________________
33. ____________________
34. ____________________
35. ____________________
36. ____________________
37. ____________________
38. ____________________
39. ____________________
40. ____________________

9. THE NEW ENGLAND STATES—I

ACROSS: ______________________________

2. The leading insurance center of the United States
5. Location of a "tea party" prior to the American Revolution
6. Location of the country's oldest Jewish house of worship, Touro Synagogue
7. Location of the Green Mountains
10. A leading center of shoemaking
12. Producer of fine tobacco
13. Location of the world's largest granite quarry
15. ______ Hampshire
16. New England state that is 90 percent forest
19. One of America's leading dairy states
21. Location of the White Mountains
25. One of America's leading poultry states
26. Large producer of lumber
27. Some of the world's highest tides occur in this New England state
28. Only New England state that doesn't touch the Atlantic Ocean
31. Producer of 60 percent of all the cranberries consumed in this country
32. Location of the easternmost point in the contiguous forty-eight states, West Quoddy Head
33. Location of the Longfellow Mountains
34. Another large producer of lumber
36. Another one of America's leading poultry states
37. Producer of high-quality cheese and butter
39. A leading center of hat making
41. Large producer of blueberries
42. A major producer of jewelry and silverware
43. Location of Cape Cod

DOWN: ______________________________

1. The leading state in the production of asbestos
3. Smallest New England state
4. First state prohibiting the sale of liquor
7. Home of America's oldest native horse breed, the Morgan horse
8. Only state in the country that borders just one other state
9. Third-largest producer of potatoes in the United States
10. The Pine Tree State
11. Location of America's first law school
14. The Lumber State
17. Location of the oldest national park east of the Mississippi River
18. Nation's largest producer of lobster
19. Location of the nation's first ski tow and chairlift
20. New England state added to the Union by the Missouri Compromise
21. Location of the highest peak in New England, Mt. Washington
22. Location of the nation's oldest active fishing port, Gloucester
23. Location of the first state lottery in the nation
24. Location of the first public school for African American children
29. Another leading center of shoemaking
30. Nation's largest producer of marble
35. Home of the first woman to serve in both houses of Congress, Margaret Chase Smith
38. The Border State
40. Rhode ______

Name ______________________ Date ______________

9. The New England States—I

Name ______________________ Date ______________________

10. THE NEW ENGLAND STATES—II

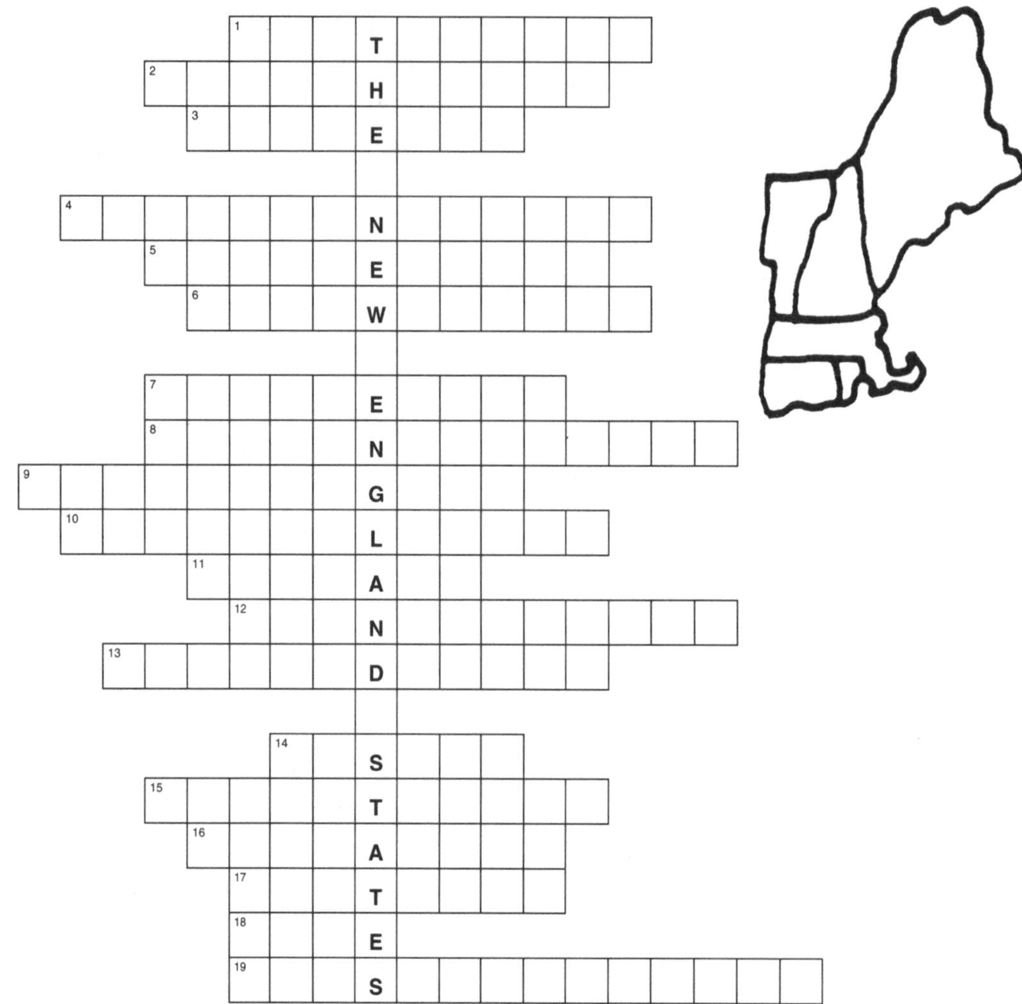

ACROSS:

1. Smallest capital city in the nation
2. First American to travel in space
3. Island in Narragansett Bay
4. U.S. president from New Hampshire
5. Naval hero of the Spanish–American War
6. Author of the first American dictionary
7. Nation's oldest active fishing port
8. U.S. president from Vermont
9. Highest peak north of the Carolinas and east of the Rocky Mountains
10. Founder of Providence and father of Rhode Island
11. Oldest college in the nation
12. Oldest women's college in the nation
13. State song of Connecticut
14. Location of the Black Heritage Trail and Beacon Hill
15. Renowned poet from New Hampshire, winner of four Pulitzer Prizes
16. U.S. president from Massachusetts
17. Location of the execution of Alse Young, the first woman to be put to death as a witch in New England
18. Famous college in Connecticut
19. Another U.S. president from Vermont

Name ______________________________ Date ____________________

11. THE NEW ENGLAND STATES—III

```
N R T F N S C H S F O R E S T R Y M W C M F
E H M L O C A A T T N O M R E V R I Y H R N
W O S G T G P J B U T T E R K M T A L E J M
H D M R S R E T S B O L R J C T L P E E V B
A E A A O L C D E G E M K E U E U D R S J H
V I D N B R O W N N E B T E T B O A I E F T
E S A I A C D C E I B E T R N M P P H I E U
N L Y T R T C J L I R A E F A K A J S A J O
E A C E E B H L L K T P Y N N D J H P D G M
T N N S N J R A A S A A D S M B I L M R N S
H D I T I L J K N P D U M R T N B U A A I T
A Y U A A P C A A A N W E P G A S M H Y D R
N T Q T M E E M H I E P D J U D T B W E L O
K R N E C C R A T S A L E M B R D E E N I P
S A H G O N B Y E P O H G A B M Y R N I U L
G P O N N E O F M G N I Y R I A D S M V B Y
I A J I N D R L J C T S O B E K H T B S P M
V E A K E I D O G E G G S L P E G A A A I O
I T R A C V E W E T N G C E Q H N T F H H U
N N P M T O R E M A S S A C H U S E T T S T
G O L E I R S R B S R A E P O D R A V R A H
N T E O C P T L B D S N I A T N U O M A B R
D S S H U H A T S U G U A P H R C B I M X O
C O N S T I T U T I O N S T A T E O C W E C
S B L U M B E R J A C K D J G N I M R A F K
M S I R U O T D H C G N I K A M T A H D F K
```

The following words are hidden in the puzzle. Words can be found horizontally, vertically, diagonally, and backward.

- lumberjack
- Cape Cod
- Yale
- Providence
- Boston Tea Party
- Ethan Allen
- lobster
- Ocean State
- Martha's Vineyard
- Maine
- shoemaking
- Harvard
- Freedom and Unity
- fishing
- New Hampshire
- Plymouth Rock
- Bay State
- Augusta
- eggs
- shipbuilding
- marble
- Concord
- Vermont
- tourism
- New Haven
- farming
- *Mayflower*
- Brown
- Massachusetts
- hat making
- Dartmouth
- Nathanael Greene
- syrup
- Portsmouth
- Granite State
- Rhode Island
- skiing
- cod
- Thanksgiving
- paper
- John Quincy Adams
- dairying
- Connecticut
- Bangor
- Salem
- Border State
- cheese
- poultry
- Boston
- mountains
- fog
- Lumber State
- butter
- forestry
- Constitution State
- Nantucket
- pears

Name ______________________________ Date ____________________

12. CONNECTICUT

ACROSS:

1. Inventor of the revolving-barrel pistol
2. State song of Connecticut
3. Location of the U.S. Coast Guard Academy
4. Revolutionary War spy who said: "I only regret that I have but one life to lose for my country"
5. Famous college in Connecticut
6. Author of *Uncle Tom's Cabin*
7. Capital city of Connecticut
8. First atomic-powered submarine, built in Connecticut
9. Location of Dinosaur State Park
10. Nickname of Connecticut
11. Author of the first American dictionary

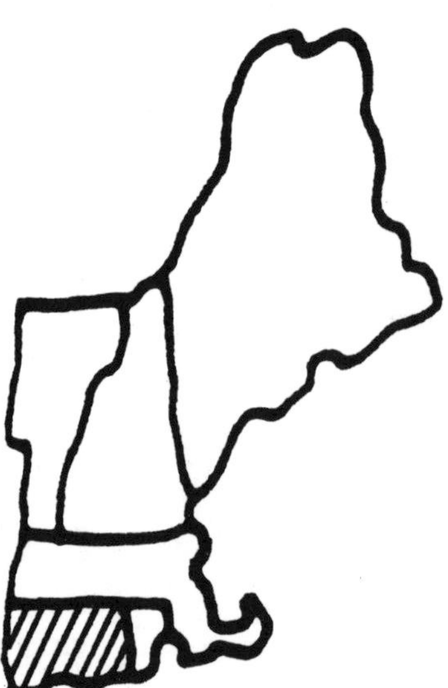

Name ______________________________ Date ____________________

13. MAINE

				1		M								
				2		A								
				3		I								
				4		N								
5						E								

ACROSS: ______________________________

1. Nickname of Maine
2. Oldest national park east of the Mississippi River
3. State bird of Maine
4. Author of *The Song of Hiawatha*
5. Nickname of Maine

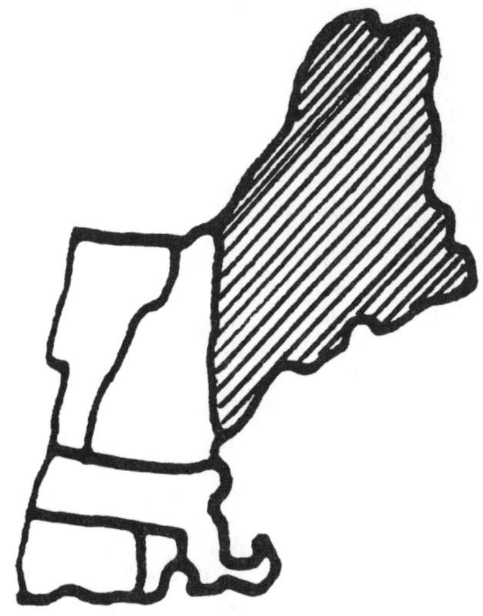

Name ______________________ Date ______________

14. MASSACHUSETTS

ACROSS: ______________________

1. Site where the Pilgrims landed in Massachusetts
2. President from Massachusetts
3. Largest city in Massachusetts
4. Nickname of Massachusetts
5. Inventor of basketball in Springfield, Massachusetts
6. Nation's oldest active fishing port
7. Oldest college in the nation
8. Another president from Massachusetts
9. Capital city of Massachusetts
10. Location of witch trials in Massachusetts
11. Oldest women's college in America
12. Popular island resort in Massachusetts
13. Famous musical director from Massachusetts

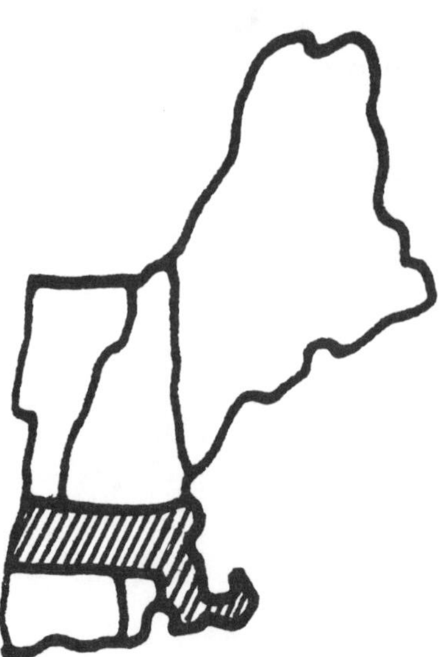

Name ______________________ Date ______________

15. NEW HAMPSHIRE

ACROSS: ______________________

1. Capital city of New Hampshire
2. State tree of New Hampshire
3. Famous U.S. senator from New Hampshire
4. Largest city in New Hampshire
5. Nickname of New Hampshire
6. Famous college in New Hampshire
7. State flower of New Hampshire
8. River in New Hampshire
9. First American to travel in space
10. President from New Hampshire
11. Renowned poet from New Hampshire
12. State bird of New Hampshire

Name ______________________________ Date ____________________

16. RHODE ISLAND

ACROSS: ____

1. Revolutionary War general from Rhode Island
2. State motto of Rhode Island
3. Famous university in Rhode Island
4. Capital city of Rhode Island
5. Composer of "The Yankee Doodle Boy" and "Over There"
6. Founder of Rhode Island
7. River in Rhode Island
8. State flower of Rhode Island
9. State tree of Rhode Island
10. Nickname of Rhode Island
11. Island in Narragansett Bay

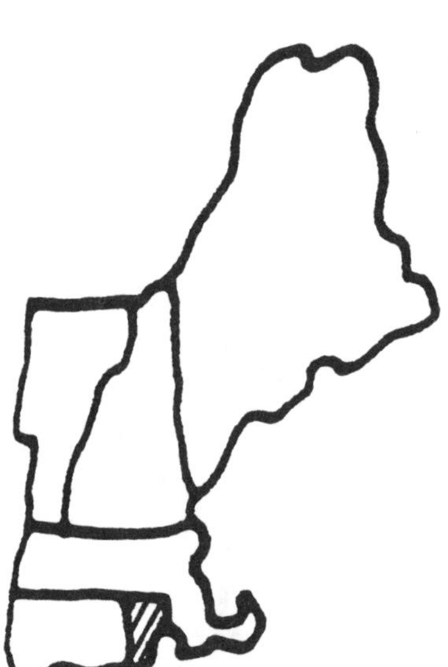

Name ______________________ Date ______________

17. VERMONT

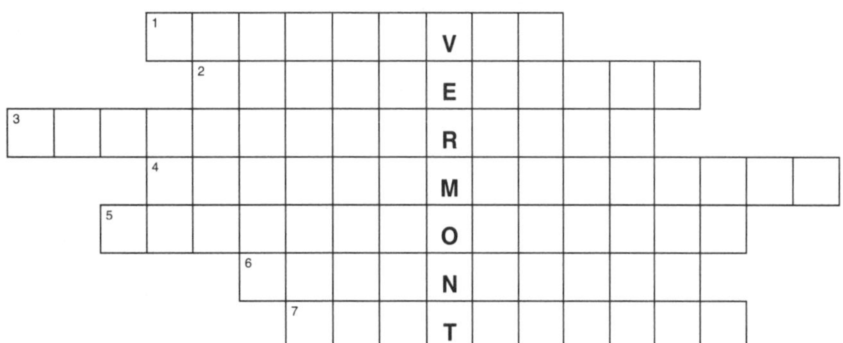

ACROSS: ______________________

1. State flower of Vermont
2. Naval hero in the Spanish–American War
3. President from Vermont
4. State motto of Vermont
5. Another president from Vermont
6. Leader of the Green Mountain Boys during the Revolutionary War
7. Smallest capital city in the nation

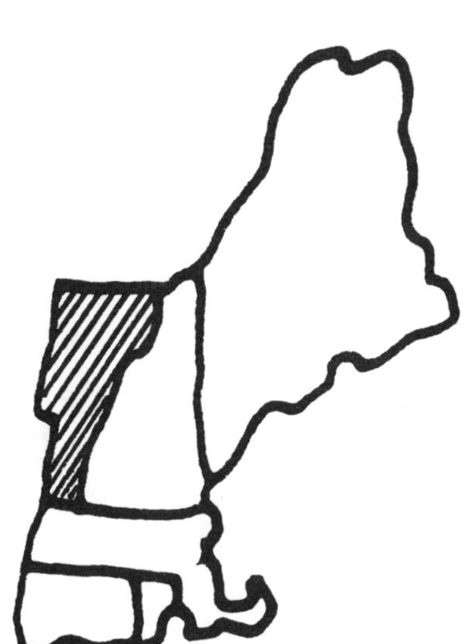

18. THE MIDDLE ATLANTIC STATES—I

ACROSS: ______

4. State that donated the land for the nation's capital
5. First and only state to be formed through secession
6. The Quaker State
7. State where "The Star-Spangled Banner" was written
9. Middle Atlantic state that allows casino gambling
11. Location of the Stock Exchange, on Wall Street
13. The Garden State
16. ______ York
19. Produces newspapers and magazines of every kind
20. Location of the nation's first national historical park
22. Smallest of the Middle Atlantic states
23. A major coal-producing state
28. Producer of 40 percent of all bituminous coal in the United States
30. One of the largest milk-producing states
32. Location of the nation's first railroad
33. A major center of the design and manufacture of clothes
34. Location of the U.S. Military Academy
35. Location of the oldest U.S. Protestant church still to hold regular services
37. The foremost producer of steel
38. State in which the first woman in America (Margaret Brent) owned land, paid taxes, and practiced law

DOWN: ______

1. First state to ratify the U.S. Constitution
2. The Free State
3. Another one of the largest milk-producing states
6. Site of the nation's first commercial oil well
8. Location of the first Indian reservation in America
10. Location of the Liberty Bell
12. Location of the first dinosaur skeleton found in North America
14. Location of the U.S. Naval Academy
15. The most mountainous state east of the Mississippi River
17. This state mines almost all the anthracite coal in the nation
18. ______ Jersey
21. Location of Thomas Edison's Menlo Park laboratory
24. Site of the first organized baseball game and intercollegiate football game
25. This state's garment industry produces nearly a quarter of the nation's clothes
26. Location of the first log cabins built in this country
27. Location of Camp David
29. Location of the Erie Canal
31. Leads the nation in the printing and publishing of books
36. ___________ Virginia

Name ______________________ Date ______________

18. The Middle Atlantic States—I

1 2 3 4 5 6 7 8 9 10 11 12 13 14 15 16 17 18 19 20 21 22 23 24 25 26 27 28 29 30 31 32 33 34 35 36 37 38

19. THE MIDDLE ATLANTIC STATES—II

ACROSS: ______________________________

1. City founded in 1625 by the Dutch, now New York City
2. Site where Francis Scott Key wrote "The Star-Spangled Banner" during the War of 1812
3. Nickname of New Jersey
4. First African American justice on the U.S. Supreme Court
5. U.S. president from New York
6. Peace-keeping organization located in New York City
7. Location of the signing of the Declaration of Independence in 1776
8. Inventor of America's first commercially successful steamboat, the *Clermont*
9. Baseball's first great home run hitter
10. Nickname of West Virginia
11. Site of the U.S. Military Academy in New York
12. Nation's most-famous monument
13. Pageant held in Atlantic City since 1921
14. Famous inventor and Founding Father of the United States
15. Nickname of Pennsylvania
16. Canal linking New York City with the Great Lakes via the Hudson River
17. Only U.S. president to serve nonconsecutive terms
18. Author of *The Good Earth*
19. Location of the National Baseball Hall of Fame and Museum
20. Island in New York purchased from Native Americans in 1626
21. Famous college in New Jersey
22. Famous inventor from New Jersey, "The Wizard of Menlo Park"
23. Location of the New York Stock Exchange

Name ______________________ Date ______________

19. The Middle Atlantic States—II

1 T
2 H
3 E

4 M
5 I
6 D
7 D
8 L
9 E

10 A
11 T
12 L
13 A
14 N
15 T
16 I
17 C

18 S
19 T
20 A
21 T
22 E
23 S

Name ______________________________ Date ____________________

20. THE MIDDLE ATLANTIC STATES—III

```
D N A L Y R A M F L L O C E A N C I T Y S
B N E J Q N T S I L O P A N N A S H R L J
E E L K U C A E E A M N N L R D O V E R L
G M I E A J I B T O E E G E M B J R V L B
R W P R K R Y R L C W B K I O T K E I A H
O E Y I E T O L B A U A R K S R C V R K A
F S N E R Y E T R F U M E L O L F O N E I
Y T A E S E C K F Q G N I Y R I A D O P N
E V B R T E S A D E L A W A R E R N S L A
L I L S A A L T D S R E K A U Q M D D A V
L R A S T O A M A A N G N I H S I F U C L
A G T H E F I R S T S T A T E M N E H I Y
V I C Y E S R E J W E N T R O Y G D J D S
P N E I T H A C A Y R T L U O P M C T K N
C I N G N I L E E H W S A R L A H H C G N
C A T S K I L L S N Y N N C T D E A W R E
A P R T C O A L O R O O T E K R D R E U P
M O A E S O K T A T T M I N I N G L S B R
O T L E C B N C N N A T C E O Y S E T S I
T O P L W E U A E L N K C R I O T S P Y N
O M A E R S R R B A L T I M O R E T O T C
P A R T E C T X G I V D T M O T E O I T E
V C K J S C S D C H A C Y Y G E L N N E T
N A V A L A C A D E M Y N O T N E R T G O
P R I N C E T O N S L L A F A R A G A I N
D E L M A R D N A L S I G N O L V A P E N
```

The following words are hidden in the puzzle. Words can be found horizontally, vertically, diagonally, and backward.

Niagara Falls
Central Park
Potomac
Gettysburg
Quaker State
Delaware
Lake Placid
Naval Academy
Trenton
Troy
Liberty Bell
dairying
Antietam

Ocean City
Hoboken
Catskills
West Virginia
Long Island
Baltimore
Atlantic City
Pennsylvania
fishing
Adirondacks
Princeton
Empire State
Maryland

Scranton
Quakers
coal
Albany
The First State
farming
Ithaca
Hudson River
Annapolis
West Point
Valley Forge
mining
Erie

Pittsburgh
New Jersey
Buffalo
steel
Wheeling
Syracuse
Newark
Dover
poultry
Charleston
New York

Name ______________________ Date ______________

21. DELAWARE

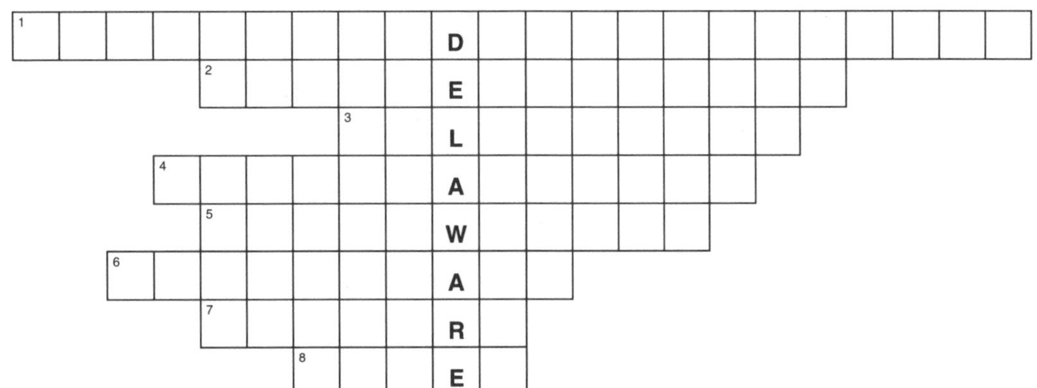

ACROSS: ______________________________

1. State motto of Delaware
2. State bird of Delaware
3. Largest city in Delaware
4. State tree of Delaware
5. Nickname of Delaware
6. Another nickname of Delaware
7. Thriving industry in Delaware
8. Capital city of Delaware

Name ______________________________ Date ____________________

22. MARYLAND

1								M							
					2			A							
				3				R							
			4					Y							
						5		L							
6								A							
		7						N							
8								D							

ACROSS: ______________________________

1. First African American justice on the U.S. Supreme Court
2. Location of the U.S. Naval Academy
3. Great baseball player from Maryland
4. State flower of Maryland
5. Largest city in Maryland
6. National anthem, written in Maryland
7. Author of *The Jungle*
8. Publisher of the *North Star*

Name ______________________________ Date ______________________

23. NEW JERSEY

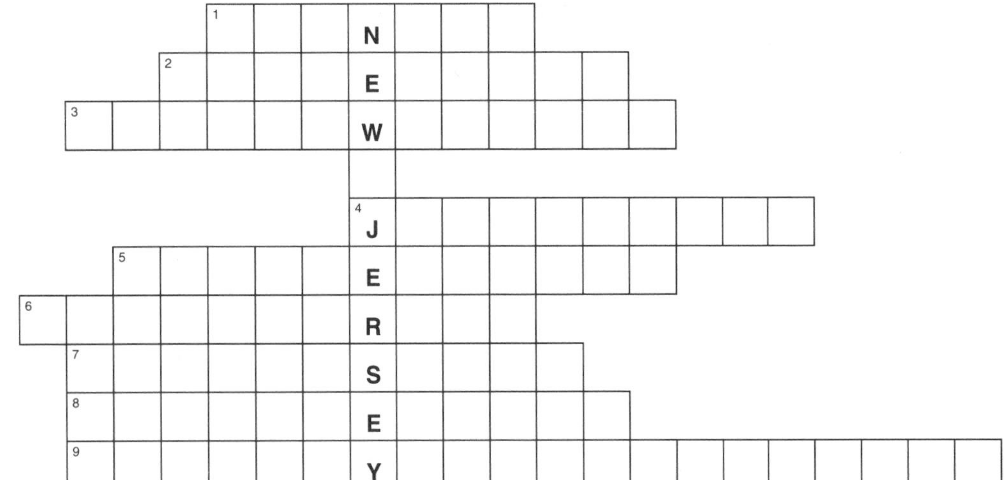

ACROSS:

1. Capital city of New Jersey
2. Dirigible that crashed in New Jersey
3. President of Princeton University before becoming president of the United States
4. City connected to New York by the Holland Tunnel
5. Author of *The Red Badge of Courage*
6. Annual pageant held in Atlantic City
7. Nickname of New Jersey
8. America's master inventor from New Jersey
9. State motto of New Jersey

Name ______________________________ Date ____________________

24. NEW YORK

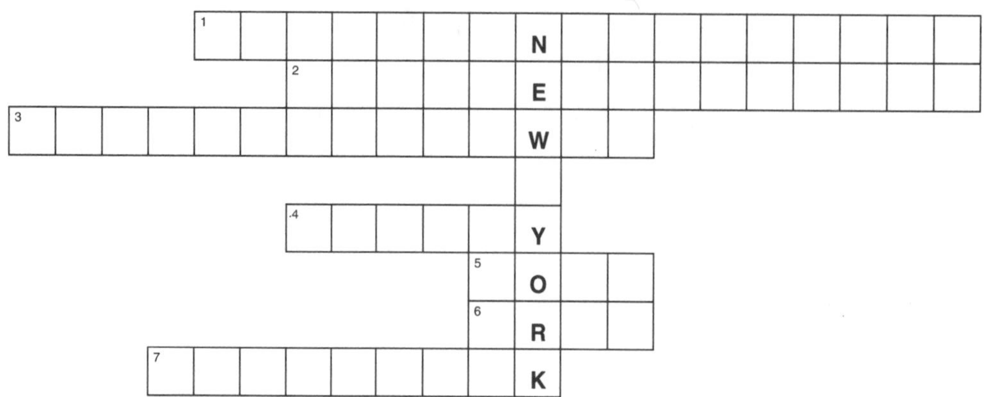

ACROSS: ______________________________

1. President from New York
2. Famous monument in New York harbor
3. Famous American composer from New York
4. Capital city of New York
5. State flower of New York
6. Canal connecting the Great Lakes to the Hudson River
7. Developed the polio vaccine

Name ________________ Date ________________

25. PENNSYLVANIA

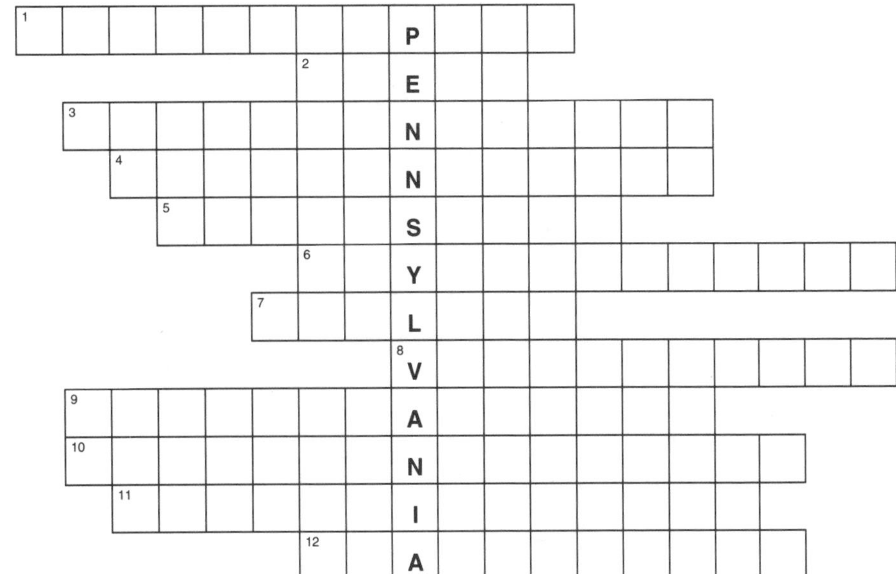

ACROSS:

1. Largest city in Pennsylvania
2. The major industry of Pennsylvania
3. First African American to sing with the Metropolitan Opera
4. Author of "My Old Kentucky Home"
5. Capital city of Pennsylvania
6. Nickname of Pennsylvania
7. State tree of Pennsylvania
8. Famous national park in Pennsylvania
9. Pennsylvania philanthropist
10. Inventor and statesman from Pennsylvania
11. State flower of Pennsylvania
12. Another nickname of Pennsylvania

Name ______________________ Date ______________

26. WEST VIRGINIA

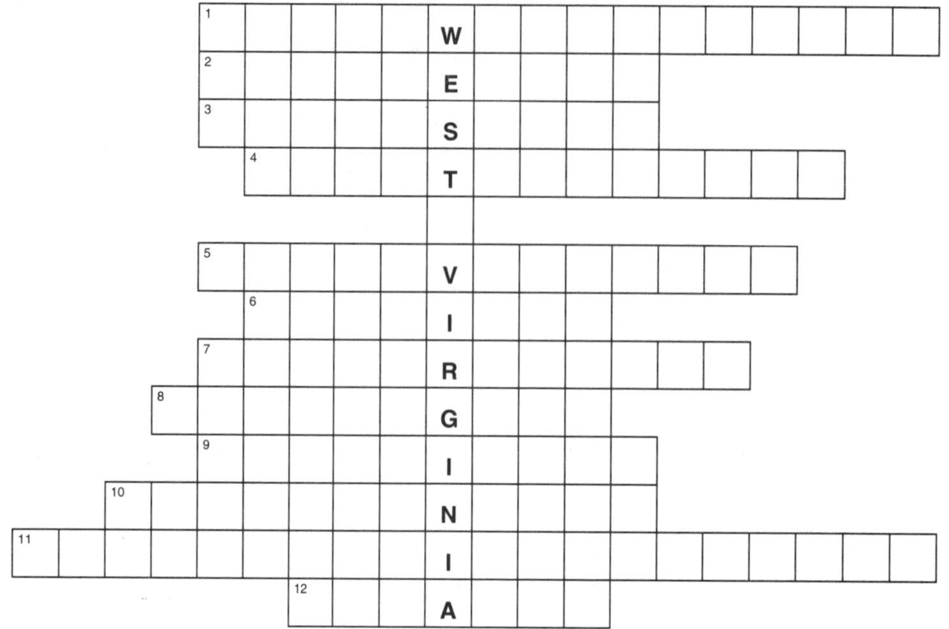

ACROSS: ______________________

1. Confederate general from West Virginia
2. Capital city of West Virginia
3. Author of *The Good Earth*
4. Nickname of West Virginia
5. National park in West Virginia
6. State bird of West Virginia
7. Location of John Brown's raid
8. Largest city in West Virginia
9. Leading industry in West Virginia
10. State flower of West Virginia
11. First African American to obtain the rank of major during the Civil War
12. River in West Virginia

27. THE SOUTHERN STATES—I

ACROSS:

3. Location of the first successful powered-airplane flight in America
7. Producer of more rice than any other state in America
8. The Magnolia State
9. Location of the world's largest known cave system
10. Calls itself the onion-growing capital of the world
12. Birthplace of Abraham Lincoln
13. Location of the assassination of Martin Luther King, Jr.
14. The Bluegrass State
20. Location of the Grand Ole Opry
21. Location of the Confederate capital of Richmond
22. Location of Mt. Vernon and Monticello
24. The Lone Star State
25. Location of the Confederate capital of Montgomery
27. State where the Civil War began
28. State with the first elected African American governor in U.S. history
30. First southern state to rejoin the Union after the Civil War
33. The Heart of Dixie State
36. State that was once an Indian territory
37. The Old Dominion
38. Producer of one of every eight broiler chickens eaten in the United States
40. The Palmetto State
41. Location of the Dust Bowl
42. Producer of almost all bauxite mined in the United States
43. The Sunshine State
44. Only place in the world where the Venus' fly-trap plant grows naturally
46. Location of the assassination of John F. Kennedy
48. The Mother of Presidents State
49. Location of the second-largest natural fresh-water body of water entirely within the United States, Lake Okeechobee
50. _____ Carolina, the first southern state to secede from the Union
51. The Sooner State

DOWN:

1. Location of Cape Canaveral and Walt Disney World
2. First in the world in the production of bourbon
3. _____ Carolina
4. Location of the oldest continuously run horse race in America
5. Location of Fort Knox, the U.S. gold depository
6. Location of Arlington National Cemetery
11. Last southern state to secede from the Union
15. Nation's leading producer of tobacco and textiles
16. Self-proclaimed poultry capital of the world
17. This state's capitol is a replica of the Greek Parthenon
18. The Volunteer State
19. Nation's leading producer of upholstered furniture
23. Only diamonds ever mined in the United States were discovered in this state
26. Location of Tuskegee Institute and the nation's first civil rights monument
29. First state to give eighteen-year-olds the right to vote
31. The Tarheel State
32. Location of one of the seven natural wonders of the world, Natural Bridge
34. The Pelican State
35. Location of the French Quarter and Mardi Gras celebration
39. The Peach State
43. Location of the nation's oldest city, St. Augustine
45. Location of the country's largest state fair
47. _____ Carolina

Name ______________________ Date ______________

27. The Southern States—I

1 2 3 4 5 6 7 8 9 10 11 12 13 14 15 16 17 18 19 20 21 22 23 24 25 26 27 28 29 30 31 32 33 34 35 36 37 38 39 40 41 42 43 44 45 46 47 48 49 50 51

Name ______________________ Date ______________

28. THE SOUTHERN STATES—II

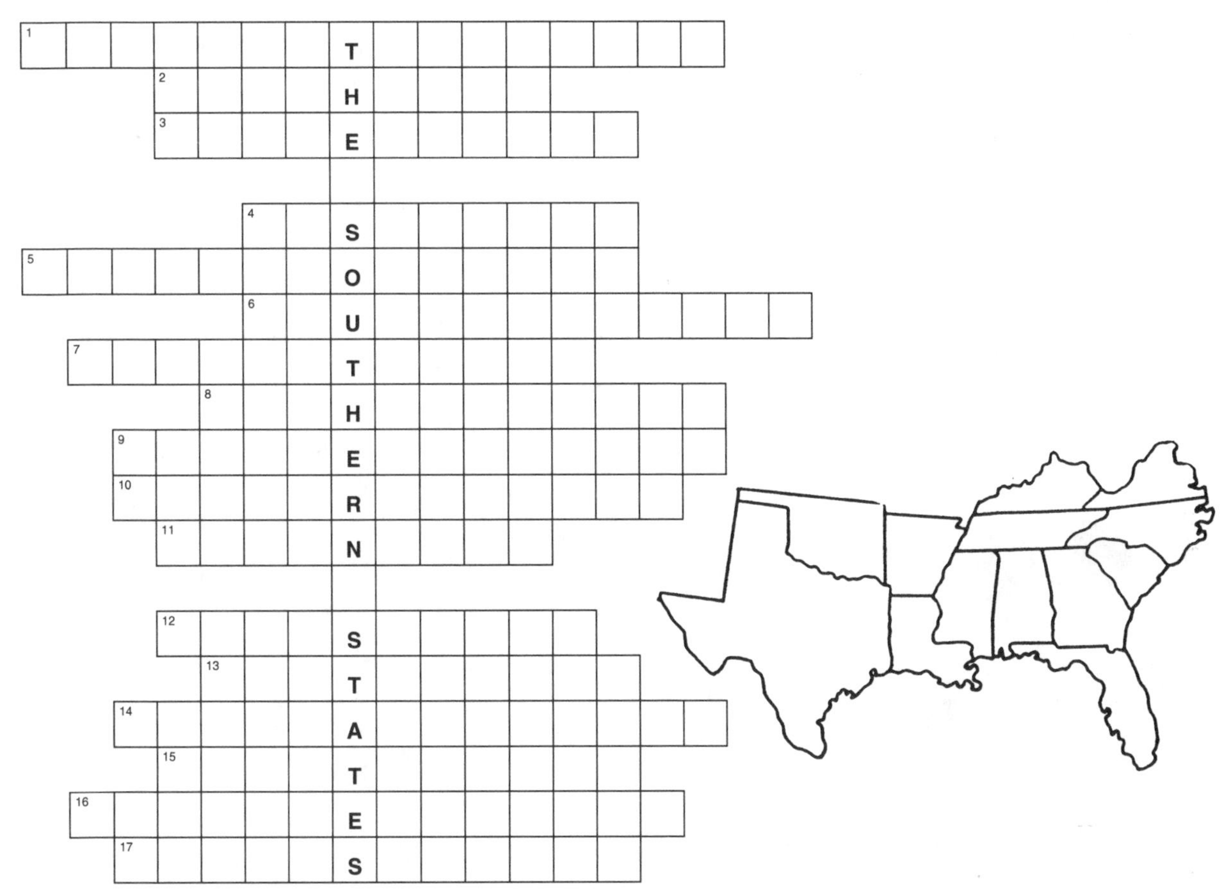

ACROSS:

1. Author of *Gone with the Wind*
2. Famous Native American athlete from Oklahoma, star of the 1912 Olympics
3. Nickname of Oklahoma
4. African American arrested for refusing to give up her seat on a Montgomery bus in 1955
5. President of the Confederate States of America
6. Highest peak east of the Mississippi River
7. Shoals off North Carolina, known as the "Graveyard of the Atlantic"
8. First African American to become an international tennis champion, winning at Wimbledon in 1957 and 1958
9. First African American to play major league baseball and the first to be inducted into the National Baseball Hall of Fame
10. U.S. president buried in Louisville, Kentucky
11. Location of the national cemetery, occupying the land once owned by Robert E. Lee
12. U.S. president buried in Nashville, Tennessee
13. Plantation home of Thomas Jefferson
14. U.S. president born in Hodgenville, Kentucky
15. Plantation home of George Washington
16. Nickname of Tennessee
17. Site where most Marine Corps recruits in the eastern United States are trained

Name ______________________________ Date ______________________

29. THE SOUTHERN STATES—III

G C A P E C A N A V E R A L S E L P P A E
B R I C E Y K C U T N E K S S A A E E S B
P I E D M O N T C E C G H E O S O C C A L
S K R A Z O B B W O N O G C A S C A A S U
S A X E T B I O R I U N R S C O H N N N E
D E F T I S R N H S A G A H R U I S S A R
A J O O K L M S T R L R C N G T M O M K I
T C X B E N I O O P G N E O S H R A I R D
N S O A G F N T K I U O L U X C B V S A G
A Y N C E Z G T D Y V R A K N A I T S U E
L S K C O C H R S C M F N F L R M E I S M
T G T O R D A L L A S O D A G O A X S T O
A M R A G M M A T E O L U I P L I A S I U
F L O R I D A E M R C K N N C I M S I N N
S O F N A M I A M I R I C E T N A A P S T
E U N S T U N A E P A A R C O A L V P U A
H I A N I L O R A C H T R O N C I A I G I
C S N L N N S S S E L I T X E T M N S A N
A I P A R M E T E N N E S S E E R N S R S
E A M O H A L K O G N O T S E L R A H C E
P N C C B E P E T R O L E U M O K H N A C
D A L L A S P M B K C O R E L T T I L N I
S S O Y B E A N S R E N O O S L U M B E R

The following words are hidden in the puzzle. Words can be found horizontally, vertically, diagonally, and backward.

Fort Knox
Graceland
Mardi Gras
peaches
Virginia
Atlanta
tobacco
Cape Canaveral
Dallas
Louisiana
Ozarks
Austin
soybeans
South Carolina
piedmont
petroleum
Texas

Great Smoky Mountains
coal
Georgia
Birmingham
sugarcane
Miami
lumber
Florida
Memphis
pecans
Blue Ridge Mountains
rice
Alabama
Charleston
cotton
Little Rock
Mississippi

Tennessee
Houston
Sooners
peanuts
Arkansas
Norfolk
North Carolina
corn
Hugo
fishing
New Orleans
Kentucky
apples
textiles
Savannah
oranges
Oklahoma

Name ______________________ Date ______________

30. ALABAMA

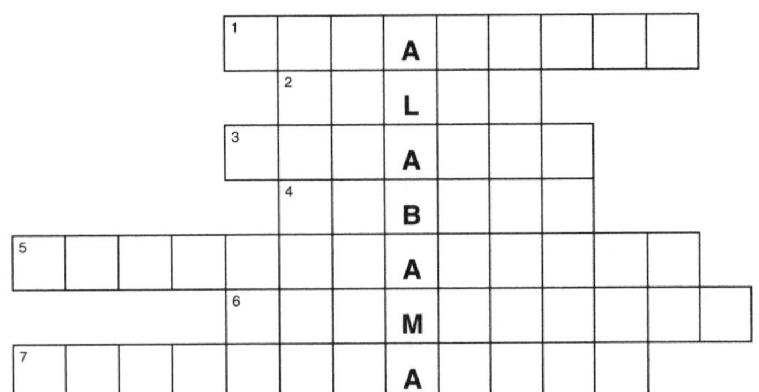

ACROSS:

1. African American woman who refused to give up her bus seat to a white man
2. Location of a civil rights march in Alabama
3. "Father of the Blues"
4. Port city in Alabama
5. Governor who was shot while campaigning for the presidency
6. Steel-producing city in Alabama
7. State bird of Alabama

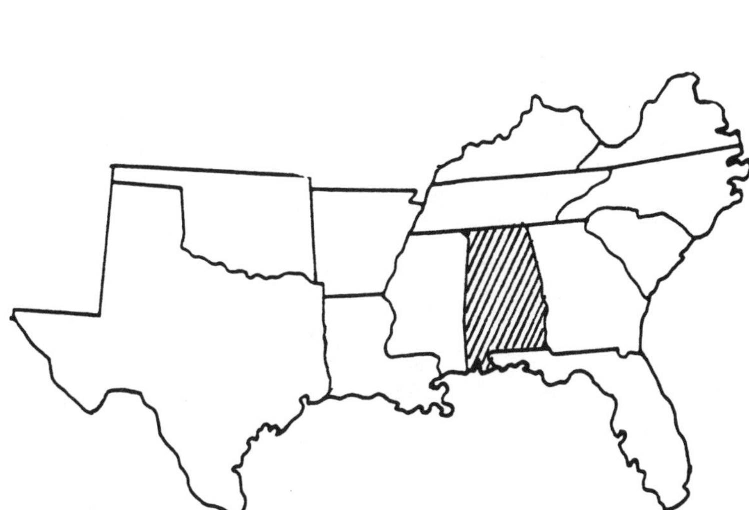

Name ______________________________ Date ____________________

31. ARKANSAS

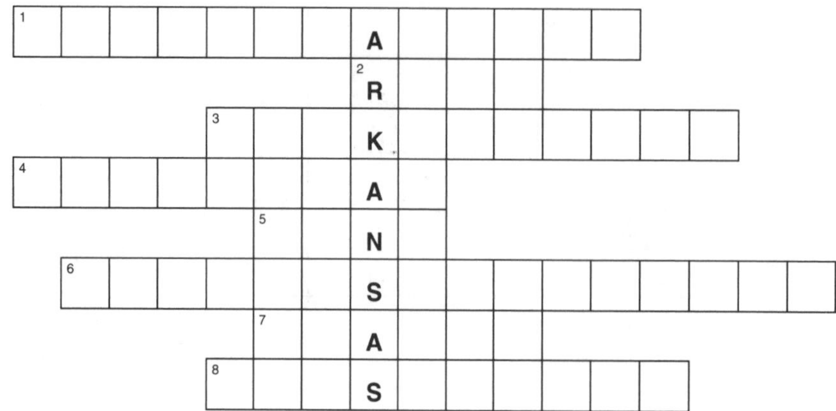

ACROSS: ______________________________

1. First woman admitted to the U.S. Senate
2. The leading crop produced in Arkansas
3. State bird of Arkansas
4. One of baseball's greatest pitchers
5. State tree of Arkansas
6. Famous World War II general from Arkansas
7. Mountains in Arkansas
8. The country's first national preserve

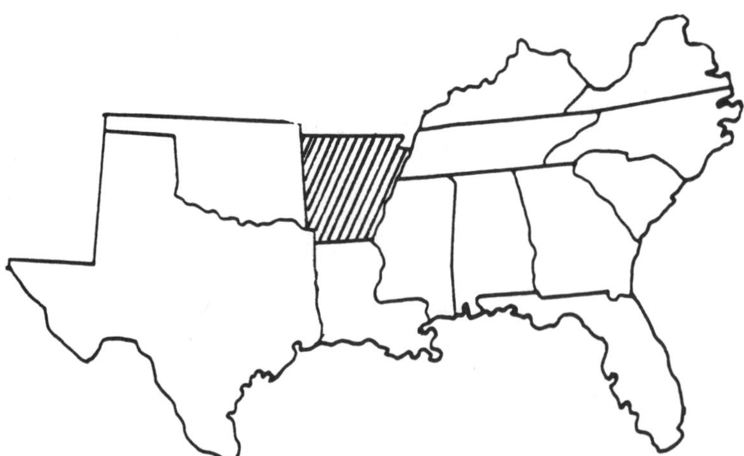

Name ______________________ Date ______________

32. FLORIDA

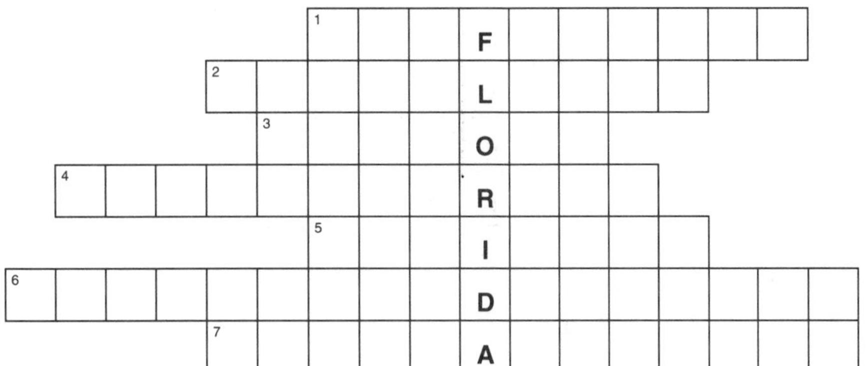

ACROSS: ______________________

1. Large swamp located in northern Florida
2. Subtropical wilderness located in Florida
3. Chief of the Florida Indians (1800–38)
4. State motto of Florida
5. Native Americans of Florida
6. Woman who organized the National Council of Negro Women and served as President Franklin Roosevelt's special adviser on minority affairs
7. NASA space center location in Florida

Name ______________________ Date ______________

33. GEORGIA

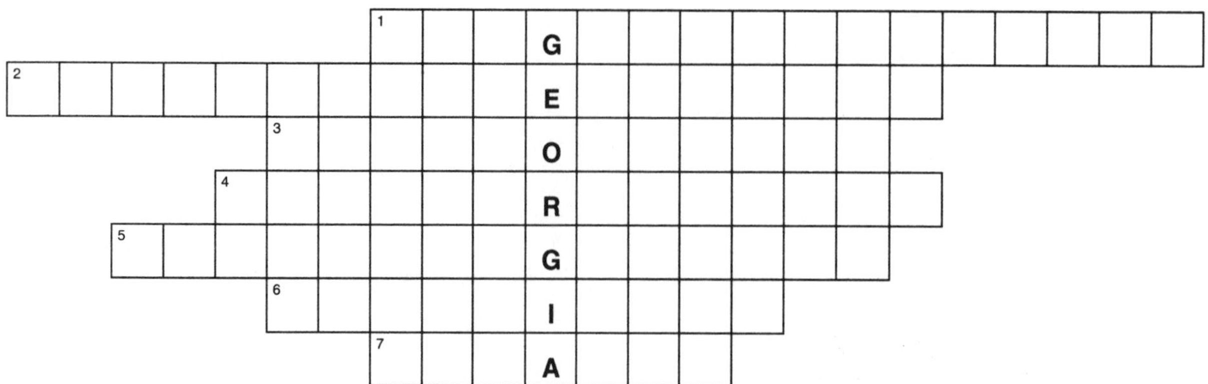

ACROSS:

1. Author of *Gone with the Wind*
2. Civil rights leader and Nobel Peace Prize winner
3. Name for the removal of the Cherokee Indians to the West
4. First African American to play major league baseball
5. Georgia's twenty-five-hundred-acre resort with a huge greenhouse
6. Inventor of the cotton gin near Savannah
7. Onion-growing capital of the world

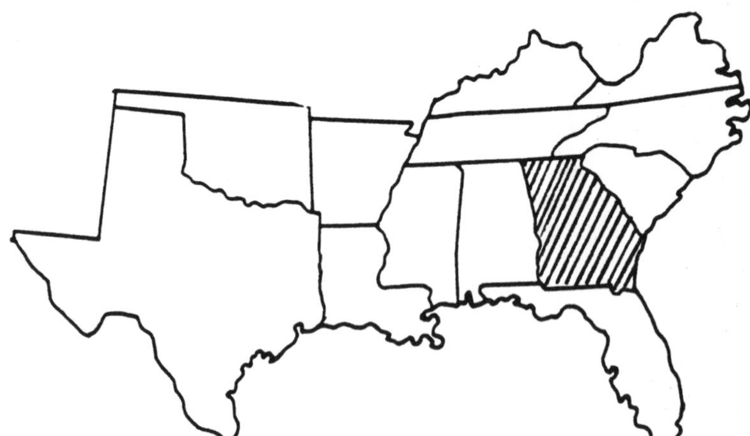

Name ______________________________ Date ____________________

34. KENTUCKY

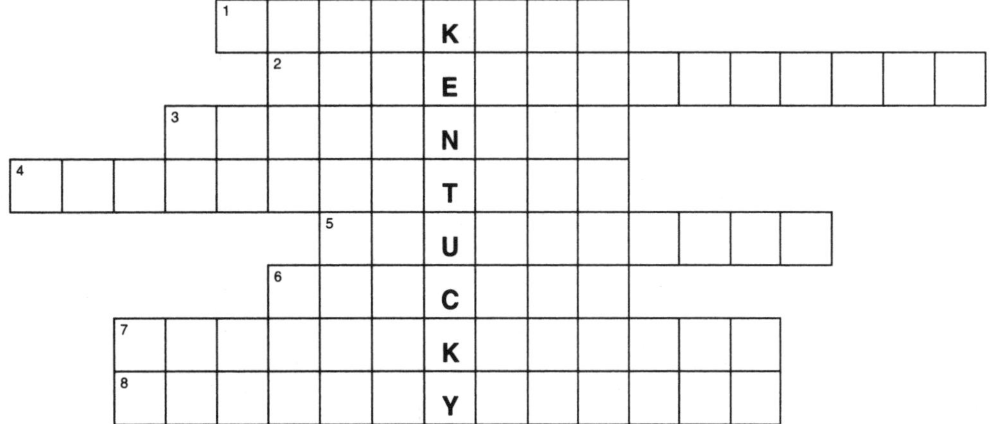

ACROSS: ______________________________

1. U.S. gold depository in Kentucky
2. Nickname of Kentucky
3. State flower of Kentucky
4. Another nickname of Kentucky
5. Largest city in Kentucky
6. President born in Kentucky
7. Oldest continuously run horse race in the country
8. President buried in Kentucky

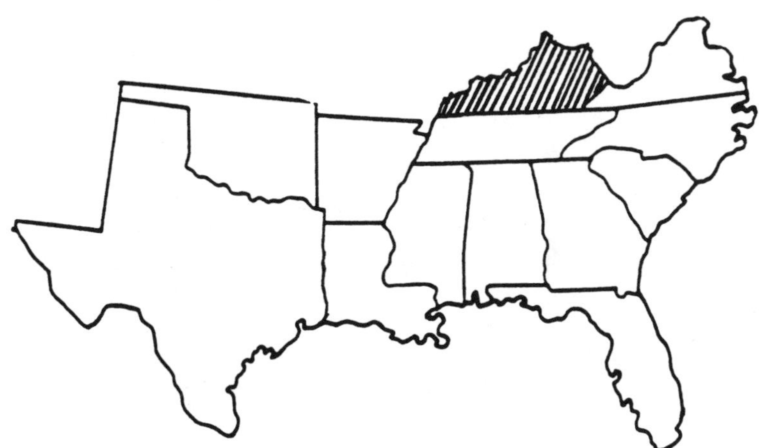

Name ______________________ Date ______________________

35. LOUISIANA

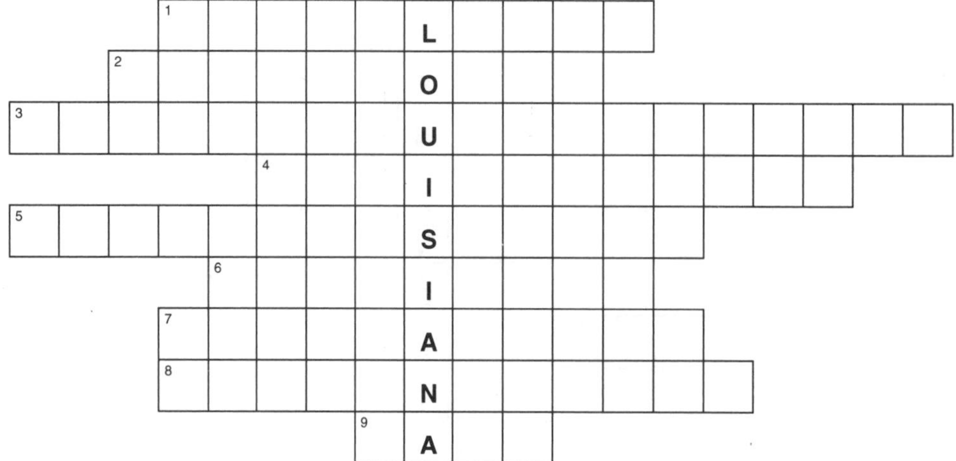

ACROSS:

1. Last battle of the War of 1812, fought in Louisiana
2. Capital city of Louisiana
3. Chief justice of the Supreme Court from Louisiana
4. Nickname of Louisiana
5. Famous trumpeter from Louisiana
6. Annual celebration in New Orleans
7. Famous pirate and smuggler from Louisiana
8. Author of *Breakfast at Tiffany's*
9. Famous music of New Orleans

Name ______________________ Date ______________

36. MISSISSIPPI

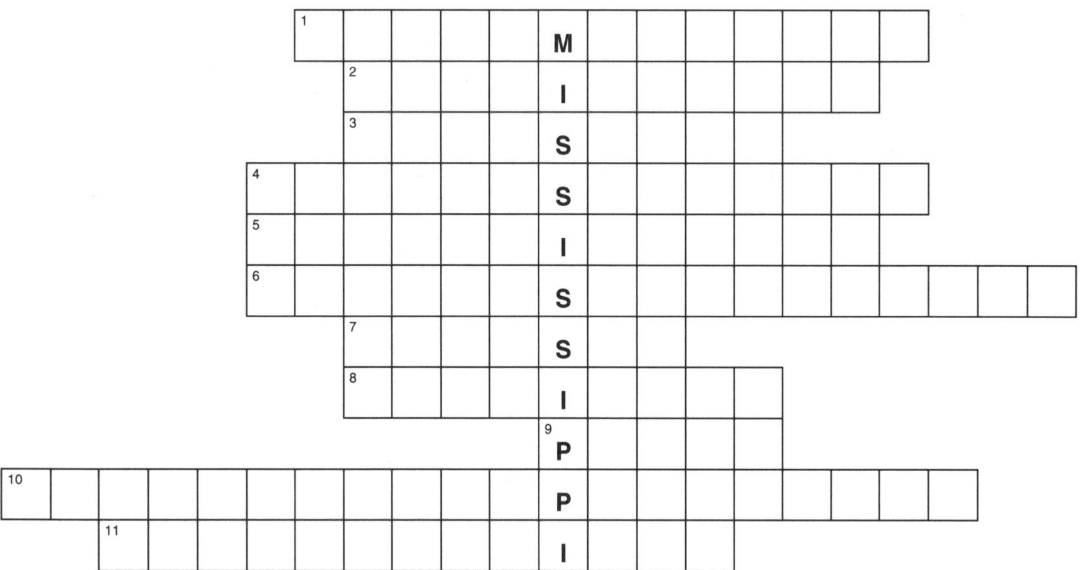

ACROSS: ______________________

1. First African American to enroll in the University of Mississippi
2. State bird of Mississippi
3. Turning-point battle of the Civil War
4. President of the Confederacy
5. Nickname of Mississippi
6. Author of *A Streetcar Named Desire*
7. Capital city of Mississippi
8. River in Mississippi
9. Another river in Mississippi
10. Annual seafood jamboree in Mississippi
11. Author of *Black Boy*

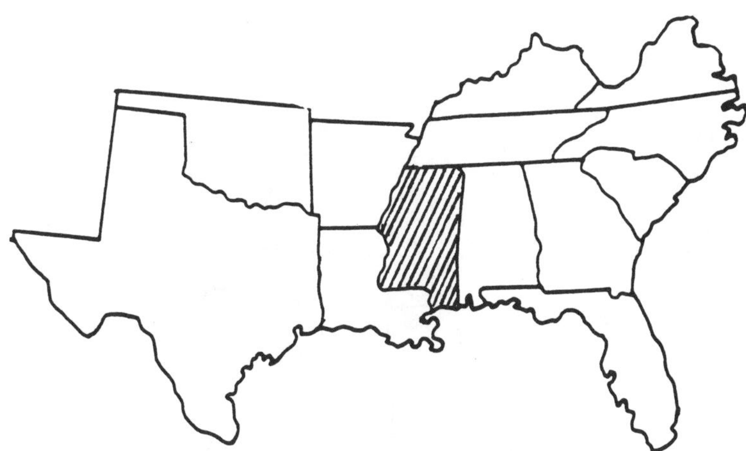

Name ______________________ Date ______________

37. NORTH CAROLINA

ACROSS:

1. State song of North Carolina
2. Made the first powered-airplane flight in America
3. Popular newscaster from North Carolina during World War II
4. Highest mountain east of the Mississippi River
5. Location of the tallest lighthouse in the country
6. Nation's leading producer of this crop
7. First Lady from North Carolina
8. Popular evangelist from North Carolina
9. First English colony in America
10. North Carolina plant that occurs in no other part of the world
11. Capital city of North Carolina
12. State bird of North Carolina
13. Author of *Look Homeward, Angel*

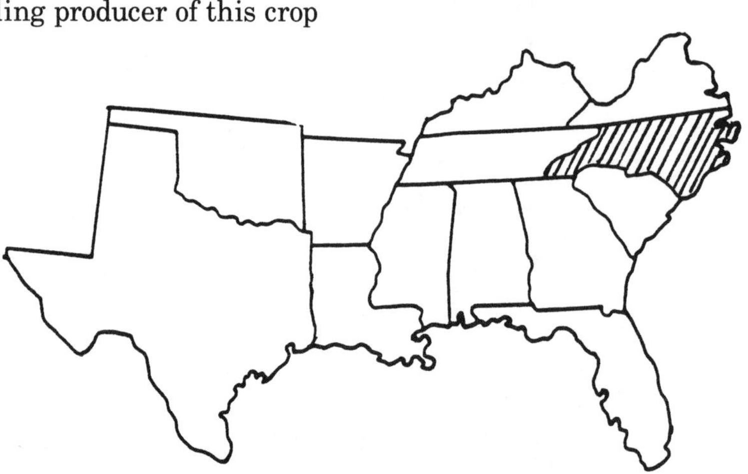

Name ________________________ Date ________________

38. OKLAHOMA

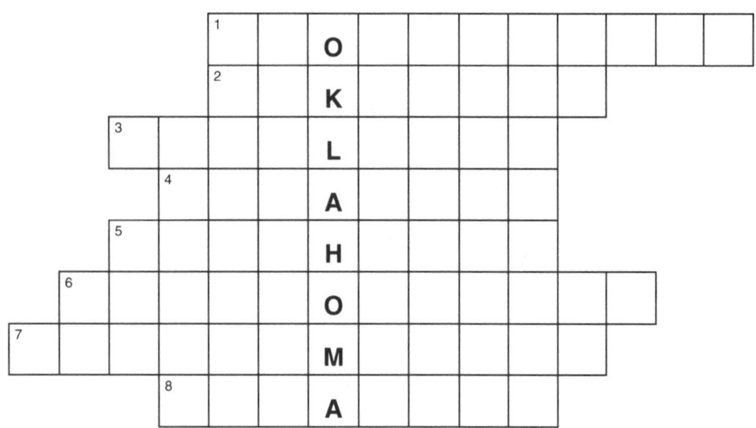

ACROSS:

1. Nickname of Oklahoma
2. River in Oklahoma
3. State flower of Oklahoma
4. Another river in Oklahoma
5. Famous Native American athlete from Oklahoma
6. Capital city of Oklahoma
7. Famous baseball player from Oklahoma
8. River in Oklahoma

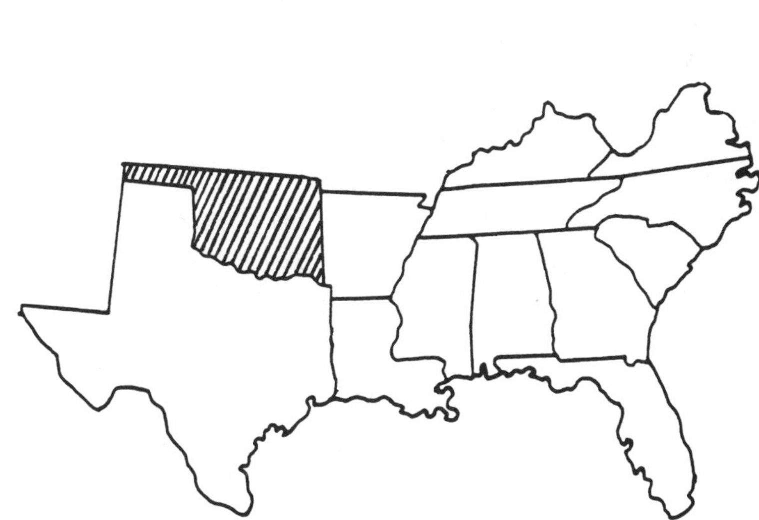

Name ______________________ Date ______________

39. SOUTH CAROLINA

ACROSS: ______________________

1. Marine Corps training center in South Carolina
2. River in South Carolina
3. Location of the first battle of the Civil War
4. State tree of South Carolina
5. Devastating hurricane that hit South Carolina in 1989
6. Crop produced in South Carolina
7. Famous South Carolina senator
8. Lake in South Carolina
9. State flower of South Carolina
10. Capital city of South Carolina
11. State bird of South Carolina
12. Another river in South Carolina
13. First African American to become an international tennis champion

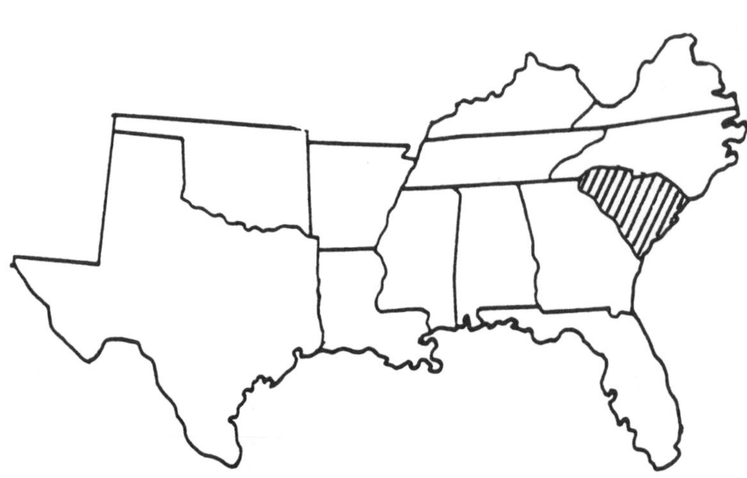

Name ______________________ Date ______________

40. TENNESSEE

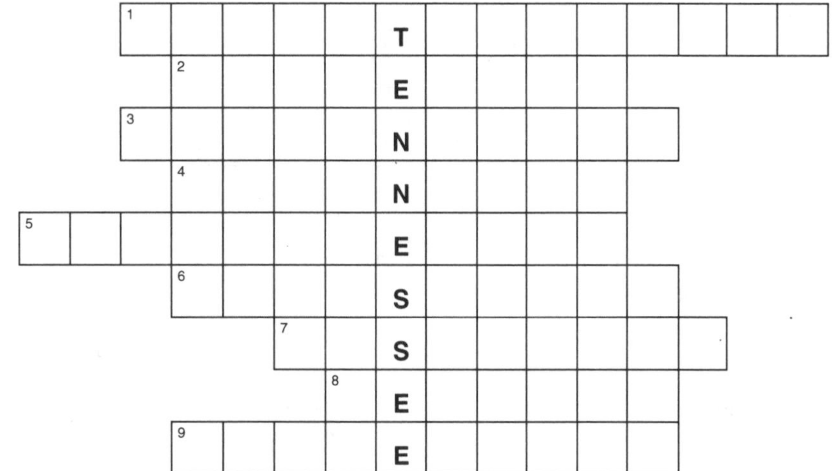

ACROSS:

1. Nickname of Tennessee
2. Estate of Elvis Presley in Tennessee
3. State bird of Tennessee
4. World War I hero from Tennessee
5. Home of country music in Tennessee
6. President buried in Tennessee
7. Capital city of Tennessee
8. Location of the assassination of Martin Luther King, Jr.
9. River in Tennessee

Name ________________________________ Date ____________________

41. TEXAS

			1			T						
			2			E						
				3		X						
					4	A						
5						S						

ACROSS: ____

1. Capital city of Texas
2. State flower of Texas
3. Country from which Texas seceded
4. Location of the assassination of John F. Kennedy
5. President of the Republic of Texas

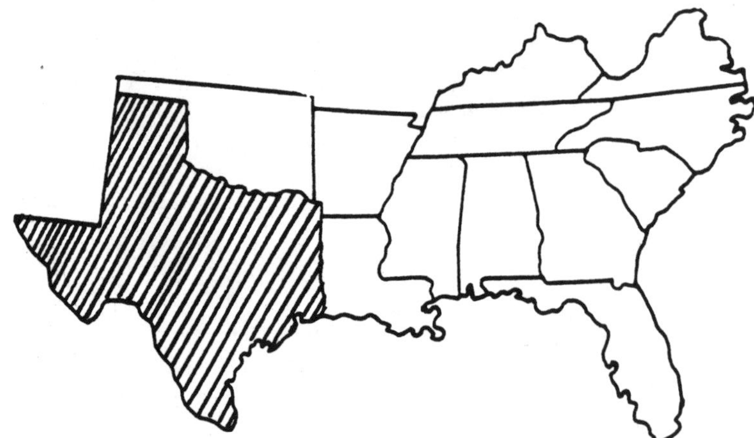

Name ______________________________ Date ____________________

42. VIRGINIA

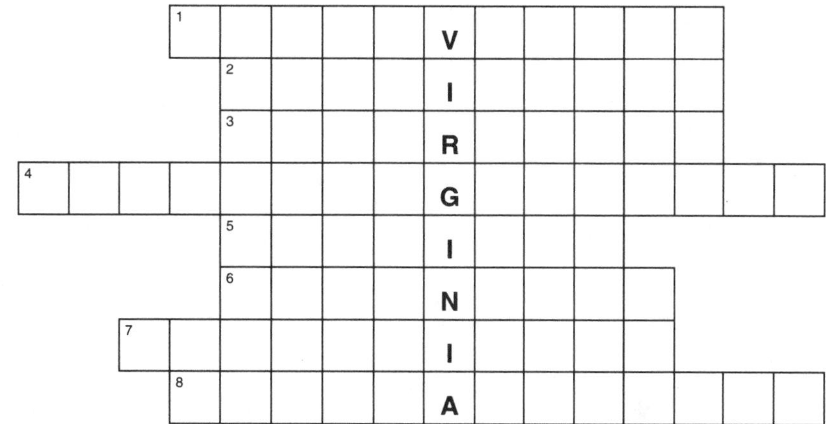

ACROSS: ____

1. Plantation home of George Washington
2. Plantation home of Thomas Jefferson
3. Confederate general in the Civil War
4. State flower of Virginia
5. State bird of Virginia
6. Location of the national cemetery
7. Nickname of Virginia
8. Author of "The Raven"

43. THE MIDWESTERN STATES—I

ACROSS:

2. Cattle outnumber people five to one in this midwestern state
5. 80 percent of this state's land is devoted to farming
7. Source of the Mississippi River is located in this state at Lake Itasca
8. Most rural state in the nation
12. The Gopher State
13. This state has the highest literacy rate in the nation
14. Nation's prime producer of milk, butter, and cheese
17. The Jayhawker State
21. Location of the nation's tallest monument
22. The Land of Lincoln
25. Location of the Mayo Clinic
26. State with the highest population of Amish people
27. The Hawkeye State
28. World's tallest building is located in this midwestern state
30. The Hoosier State
33. Home of the mythical hero Paul Bunyan and his blue ox, Babe
35. Only state with a unicameral legislature
38. Location of Mount Rushmore
40. State that passed the nation's first unemployment compensation act
41. The Sioux State

DOWN:

1. ______ Dakota, the Blizzard State
3. State that passed the first law in the country to preserve archeological wonders
4. The Sunflower State
5. First in the production of corn, hogs, and oats
6. Geographic center of the contiguous states
9. The Buckeye State
10. First state to pass a ban on alcohol
11. State with the highest average wind speed in the United States
14. The Badger State
15. State with the nation's first coeducational college, Oberlin
16. World's most devastating tornado struck this state in 1925
18. The Prairie State
19. World's leading producer of breakfast cereals
20. The Wolverine State
23. Home of the legendary Johnny Appleseed
24. The Cornhusker State
29. First in the production of poultry, eggs, and cattle
30. First electronic digital computer built in this state in 1939
31. The painting *American Gothic* depicts farm people from this state
32. The Show Me State
34. State with the world's first professional baseball team
36. The leading producer of helium
37. Seven natives of this state have become U.S. presidents
39. The Corn State

Name ______________________ Date ______________

43. The Midwestern States—I

1 2 3 4 5 6 7 8 9 10 11 12 13 14 15 16 17 18 19 20 21 22 23 24 25 26 27 28 29 30 31 32 33 34 35 36 37 38 39 40 41

Name ______________________ Date ______________

44. THE MIDWESTERN STATES—II

ACROSS:

1. Automotive capital of the United States
2. Gold was discovered here in 1874, sacred land of the Sioux Indians
3. Nickname of Indiana
4. Name of a city and river in Michigan
5. U.S. president buried in Kansas
6. U.S. president from Illinois
7. Nickname of Iowa
8. Site of the world's leading producer of breakfast cereals
9. Location of the huge images of four presidents in South Dakota
10. U.S. president from Missouri
11. Nickname of Michigan
12. Nickname of Minnesota
13. Nickname of Kansas
14. Nickname of Wisconsin
15. U.S. president from Iowa
16. World-renowned medical center in Minnesota
17. World's tallest building, 1,454 feet high
18. First woman to fly solo across the Atlantic Ocean
19. Nickname of Nebraska

Name ______________________________ Date ____________________

45. THE MIDWESTERN STATES—III

```
B S A F D A I R Y I N G A O O G A C I H C
G R E A T L A K E S K B K I O W A N N E I
A T O K A D H T U O S L O H M H D K D T N
R A S D N A T I H C I W I O A I J Y I T C
Y I I N C A F O G M R H H M A H T K A A I
C R O A T O K A D H T R O N S I W M N L N
S O N L S L R E R G B L A I C K I C A P N
C E I E I Y A N P G A P M S A S S O S H A
C P L V B N N O C O O A A N H W C R A A T
N M L E E R C T C L T S S O H I O N M S I
L I I L O E A O I C N A H S B S N I P T P
O N G C V E K S L A S I A U U A S R O P A
C N N B H N C U K N O B T B K S I S M A I
N E I W M I L K A A A T M S O N N K A U P
I S S F A R G O W W E U A U G Y S C H L I
L O N O S I D A M R L R R F D C S O A M E
F T A F A F G O N O B I I M U T C T I W R
O A L E S E E H C E S E M J L V T S O A R
D E T R O I T I N K L I M O U E B E W W E
N G A B A D L A N D S B U T T E R V A O N
A H A M O G A B E N N I W C H G N I B I J
L C F E S K C R A M S I B B R T O L E D O
```

The following words are hidden in the puzzle. Words can be found horizontally, vertically, diagonally, and backward.

Land of Lincoln
Badlands
Nebraska
Indianapolis
Chicago
Wichita
Ohio
Lansing
dairying
Madison
Omaha
Indiana
Kansas City

Pierre
Columbus
cheese
Michigan
Milwaukee
Boys Town
Illinois
Great Lakes
Bismarck
St. Louis
wheat
Wisconsin
milk

Winnebago
Springfield
St. Paul
Missouri
Toledo
Wabash
South Dakota
livestock
Amish
North Dakota
corn
Topeka
Iowa

Cincinnati
Gary
Lincoln
Peoria
Minnesota
Duluth
Fargo
butter
Detroit
Kansas
Cleveland
Platte

Name ______________________ Date ______________

46. ILLINOIS

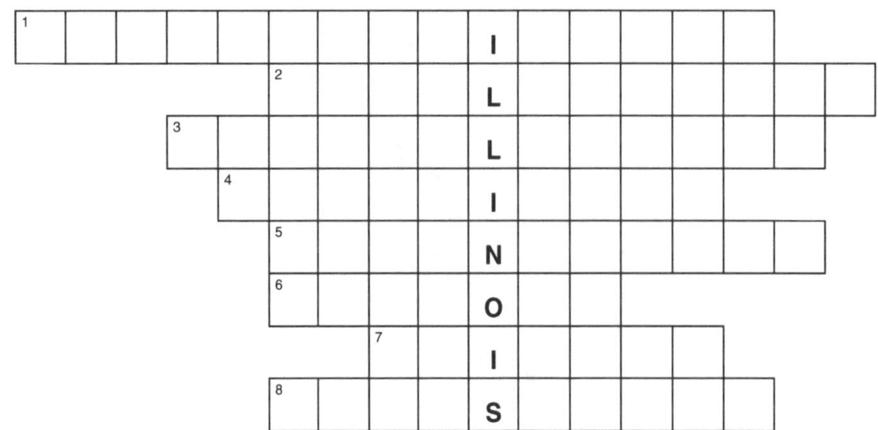

ACROSS:

1. Author of *The Sun Also Rises*
2. President born in Illinois
3. Nickname of Illinois
4. Famous creator of animated cartoons, from Illinois
5. Capital city of Illinois
6. President who resided in Illinois
7. Largest city in Illinois
8. World's tallest building

Name ______________________________ Date ____________________

47. INDIANA

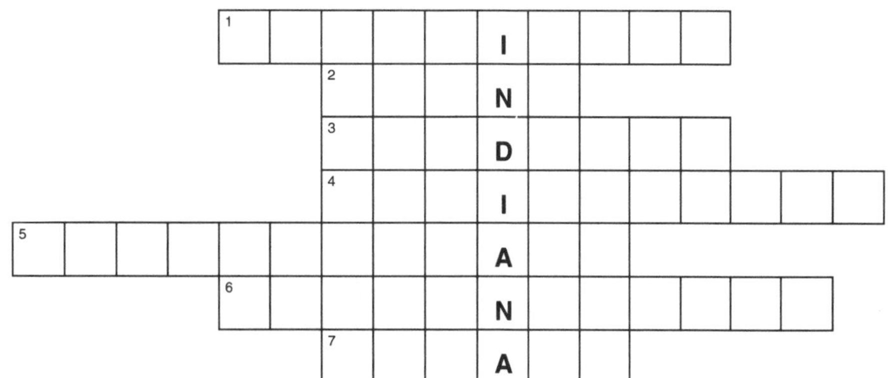

ACROSS: ______________________________

1. Astronaut killed in a fire during a flight simulation
2. State flower of Indiana
3. State bird of Indiana
4. State tree of Indiana
5. Nickname of Indiana
6. Location of a world-famous auto race
7. River in Indiana

Name ______________________ Date ______________

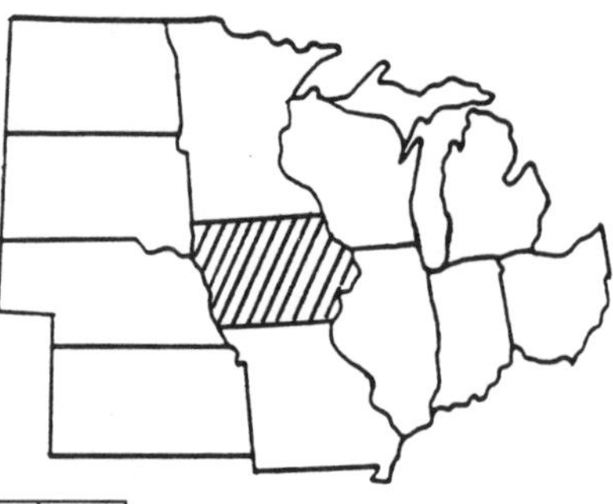

48. IOWA

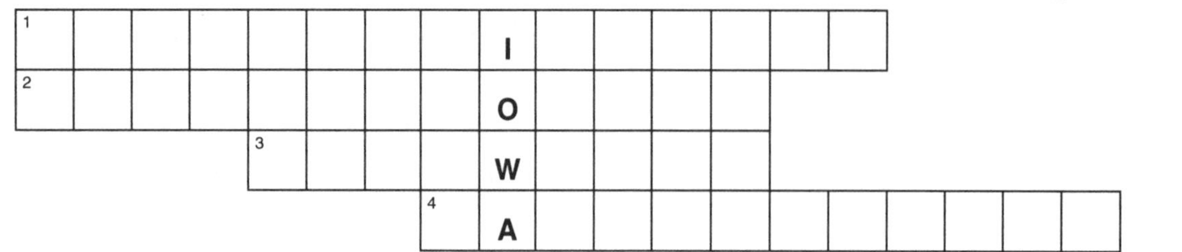

ACROSS:

1. Famous frontier scout who started a Wild West show
2. First president born west of the Mississippi River
3. Famous actor of western and action movies
4. Nickname of Iowa

49. KANSAS

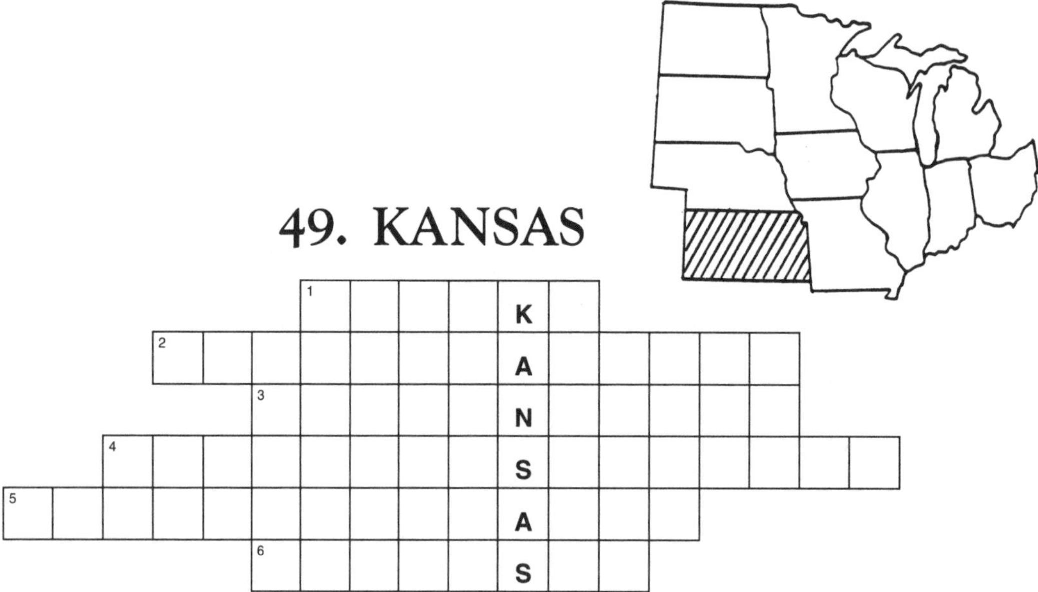

ACROSS:

1. Capital city of Kansas
2. Famous female aviator from Kansas
3. Famous temperance advocate from Kansas
4. President buried in Kansas
5. State song of Kansas
6. River in Kansas

Name ____________________ Date ____________________

50. MICHIGAN

		1				M							
	2					I							
3						C							
		4				H							
5						I							
6						G							
7						A							
				8		N							

ACROSS: ____________________

1. River in Michigan
2. Largest city in Michigan
3. World's leading producer of breakfast cereals
4. Creator of Cornflakes, to serve as a breakfast dish
5. Nickname of Michigan
6. Capital city of Michigan
7. State bird of Michigan
8. Inventor of the Model T automobile, in 1913

Name ______________________________ Date ______________________

51. MINNESOTA

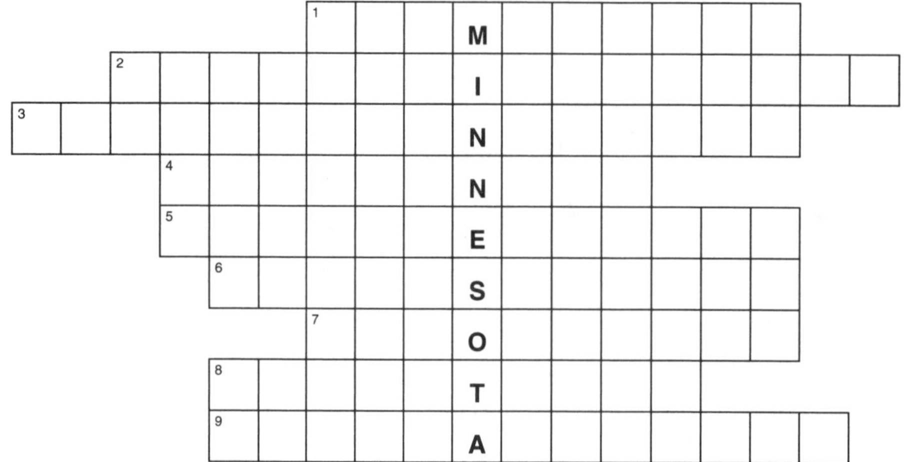

ACROSS: ____

1. State bird of Minnesota
2. Author of *The Great Gatsby*
3. Aviator who made the first solo flight across the Atlantic Ocean
4. Mythical lumberjack hero with his blue ox, Babe
5. Chief justice of the Supreme Court from Minnesota
6. State flower of Minnesota
7. Renowned medical center in Minnesota
8. Source of the Mississippi River
9. First American to win the Nobel Prize for literature

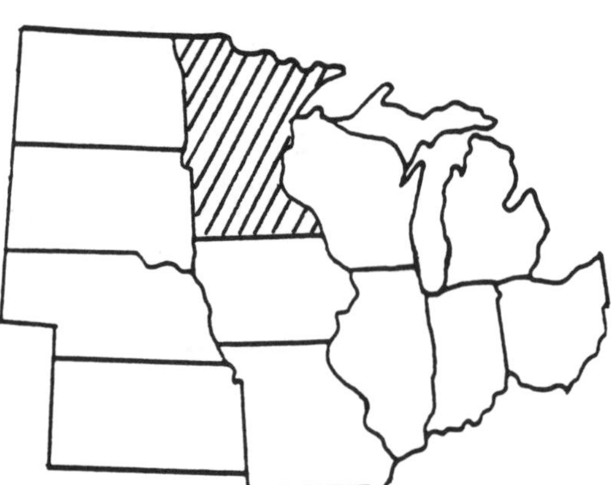

Name ______________________ Date ______________

52. MISSOURI

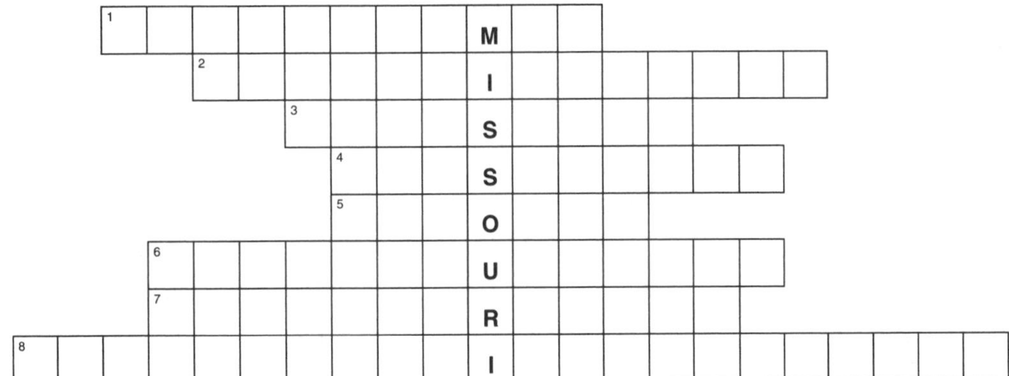

ACROSS:

1. President from Missouri
2. African American entertainer from Missouri who achieved fame in Paris during the late 1920s
3. Missouri slave who sued for his freedom
4. Leader of a notorious outlaw gang in Missouri
5. Largest city in Missouri
6. Endower of prestigious prizes for achievement
7. World War I general from Missouri
8. African American scientist who discovered new uses for the peanut and sweet potato

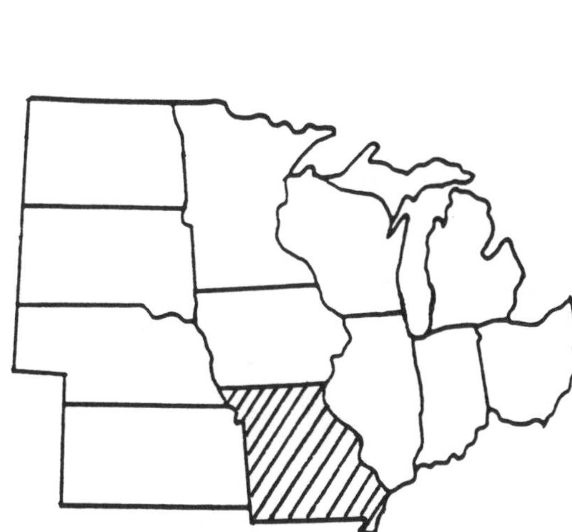

Name ______________________ Date ______________

53. NEBRASKA

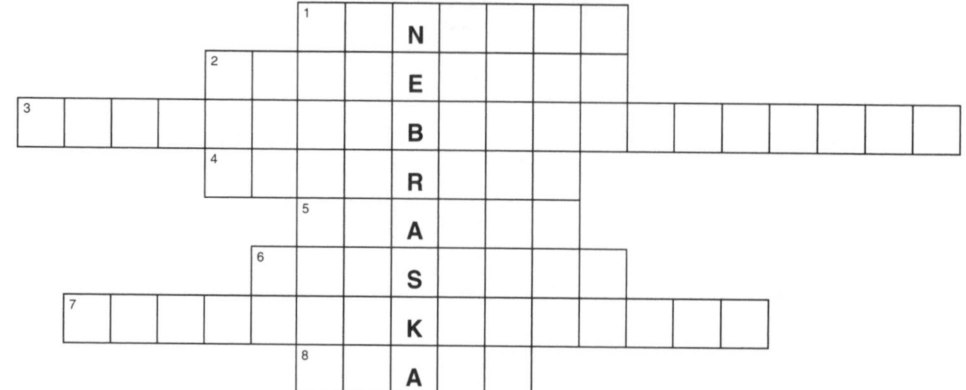

ACROSS: ______________________________

1. Capital city of Nebraska
2. State flower of Nebraska
3. State motto of Nebraska
4. River in Nebraska
5. Another river in Nebraska
6. Home for children, started by Father Flanagan
7. Nickname of Nebraska
8. Largest city in Nebraska

Name ______________________ Date ______________

54. NORTH DAKOTA

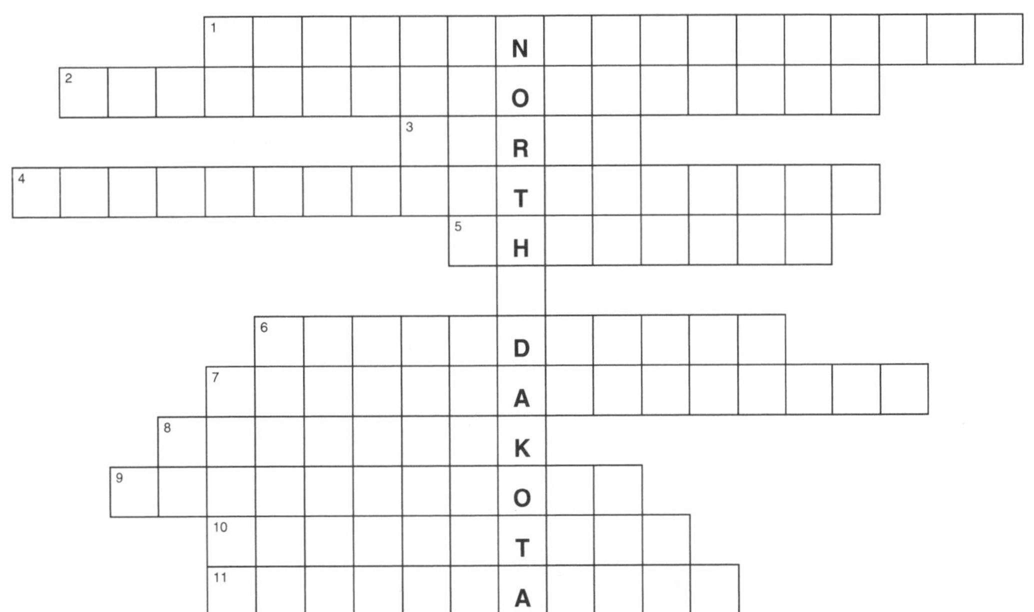

ACROSS:

1. State bird of North Dakota
2. National Park in North Dakota
3. Largest city in North Dakota
4. River in North Dakota
5. Another river in North Dakota
6. Scenic wasteland area in North Dakota
7. State flower of North Dakota
8. Capital city of North Dakota
9. North Dakota author of western novels
10. Nickname of North Dakota
11. State tree of North Dakota

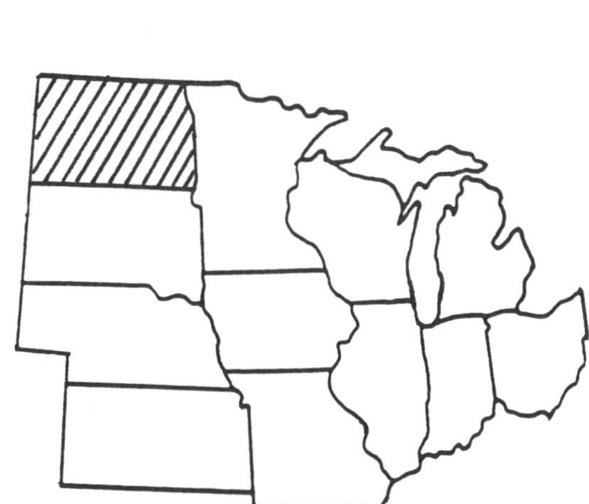

Name ____________________ Date ____________

55. OHIO

ACROSS: ____________________

1. Nation's first coeducational college
2. Religious sect in Ohio
3. State bird of Ohio
4. Capital city of Ohio

56. SOUTH DAKOTA

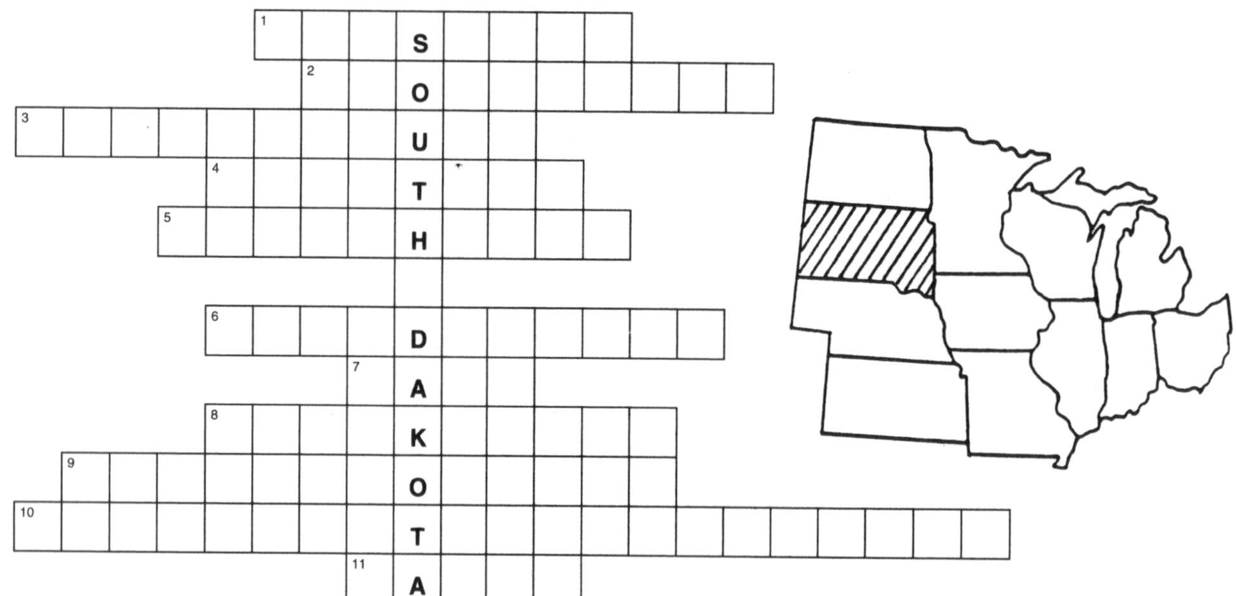

ACROSS: ____________________

1. River in South Dakota
2. Largest city in South Dakota
3. Famous chief of the Sioux Indians
4. Lake in South Dakota
5. Famous chief of the Sioux Indians
6. Site of an Indian massacre in 1890
7. Another lake in South Dakota
8. Sacred land of the Sioux Indians in South Dakota
9. Creator of the Mt. Rushmore National Memorial
10. State motto of South Dakota
11. Another river in South Dakota

Name ______________________ Date ______________

57. WISCONSIN

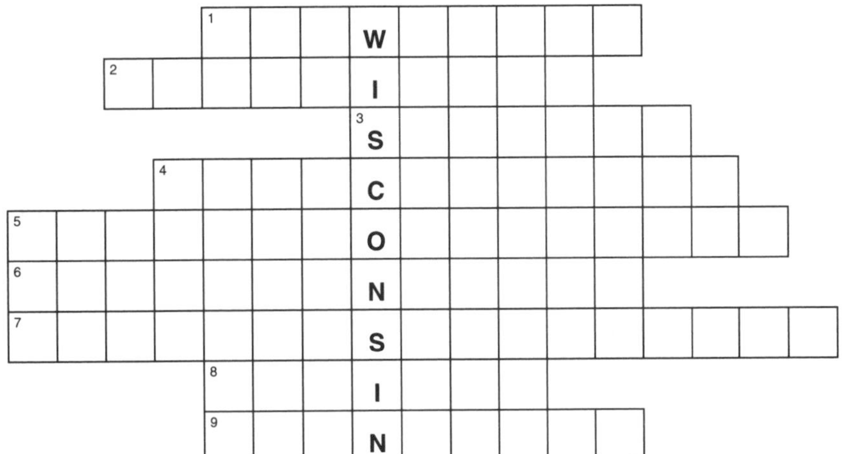

ACROSS:

1. Largest city in Wisconsin
2. State flower of Wisconsin
3. River in Wisconsin
4. Famous actor from Wisconsin
5. Famous architect from Wisconsin
6. State bird of Wisconsin
7. Nickname of Wisconsin
8. Capital city of Wisconsin
9. Lake in Wisconsin

58. THE ROCKY MOUNTAIN STATES—I

ACROSS: ______________________________

1. Fewer people live here than in any other state
5. The first state to give women the right to vote
11. The driest state in the Union
13. Big Sky Country
15. The Centennial State
16. The Grand Canyon State
18. Location of the world's first national park
20. Location of the U.S. Air Force Academy
24. The Silver State
25. Location of the Petrified Forest
26. Has the highest average elevation of any state
27. Gambling was legalized here in 1869
28. Location of Lake Tahoe
29. Location of the Great Salt Lake

DOWN: ______________________________

2. The Land of Enchantment
3. Location of Custer's Last Stand, at the Little Bighorn River
4. Location of Pike's Peak
6. The Gem State
7. Site of the first U.S. nuclear power plant
8. Location of Glacier National Park
9. Location of the first atomic bomb testing
10. The Beehive State
12. Location of the Painted Desert
14. Last of the contiguous forty-eight states added to the Union
17. The Rocky Mountain State
18. The Cowboy State
19. Location of Lake Mead and Hoover Dam
21. Location of the oldest continuously occupied spot in the United States, Oraibi
22. Location of the largest wilderness preserve in the contiguous United States
23. State famous for growing potatoes
24. The Sagebrush State

Name ______________________ Date ______________________

58. The Rocky Mountain States—I

59. THE ROCKY MOUNTAIN STATES—II

ACROSS:

1. Famous geyser in Yellowstone National Park
2. Nickname of Utah
3. Nation's gambling capital
4. Colorful fur trapper and guide, "King of the Mountain Men"
5. First woman justice on the U.S. Supreme Court
6. One of the natural wonders of the world, located in Arizona
7. Famous painter who derived inspiration from New Mexico's landscape
8. Nickname of Montana
9. Nickname of Idaho
10. Location of the U.S. Air Force Academy
11. Nickname of Wyoming
12. Least-populated state in the nation
13. Largest alpine lake in North America
14. Mormon leader who established the community in Salt Lake City
15. Nickname of Colorado
16. Nickname of New Mexico
17. World's first national park, established in 1872
18. Nickname of Nevada
19. Famous trapper, guide, and Indian agent in New Mexico
20. Mountain range in western Wyoming, famous for its abundant wildlife
21. Driest state in the nation
22. One of the West's most famous mountains

Name ______________________ Date ______________

59. The Rocky Mountain States—II

1 T
2 H
3 E

4 R
5 O
6 C
7 K
8 Y

9 M
10 O
11 U
12 N
13 T
14 A
15 I
16 N

17 S
18 T
19 A
20 T
21 E
22 S

Name ______________________________ Date ____________________

60. THE ROCKY MOUNTAIN STATES—III

```
L N S N O G W M B I V D L O G S P N Y F L
E O S K O T W L O A H E T K I E R E E O U
S M G L I Y E F I N O Y R C C O O P L U F
I G D G O I N L S A T E R O A T V S L R H
O L N M I L N A E I V A P R G A O A A C T
B O I I D N N G C L N P N R O T N N V O I
D N O M L E G E I E E O E A N O E E N R A
G H D H O L K S V R C T S L Z P W L U N F
A A A T G A I U O A T Y S I C O M E S E D
M T R M L D L B T U D N R E B I E H T R L
U U O T A G O B B A O A T B N H X Y E S O
Y R L H M E A A U M H C S I I S I T I S D
O A O F U R N T R Q A T N P O S C I H A H
S X C C Y O E O I T U G D J E Y O C O G L
R A I O K N M C T C O E A O U N R N O E A
F R N N U I N L S L N V R M R E N O V V K
O E R T E M E O D V A T A Q N R S S E S E
R V E Y A O N S E N R E N O U F E R R A T
E N P O U F H R C H E Y E N N E I A D L A
S E S S H E E P R E L O H N O S K C A J H
T D A D E V I L S T O W E R S C C O M R O
R E C P S N W O T T S O H G P R O V O A E
Y E L L O W S T O N E K I T C A R S O N D
```

The following words are hidden in the puzzle. Words can be found horizontally, vertically, diagonally, and backward.

Salt Lake City
Rockies
ghost towns
Wyoming
Reno
Bryce Canyon
Boise
forestry
Santa Fe
Nevada
Sun Valley
Helena
Kit Carson
sheep

Casper
copper
Montana
Denver
O.K. Corral
Jackson Hole
Cheyenne
cattle
Tucson
Colorado
Provo
mining
Navajos
Yellowstone

Four Corners
Vail
bison
Arizona
gold
Butte
Carson City
Devils Tower
Las Vegas
Geronimo
Lake Tahoe
logging
Utah
potatoes

Aspen
Hoover Dam
Albuquerque
Mormons
silver
New Mexico
skiing
Old Faithful
Billings
Yuma
Idaho
Phoenix

Name ______________________ Date ______________

61. ARIZONA

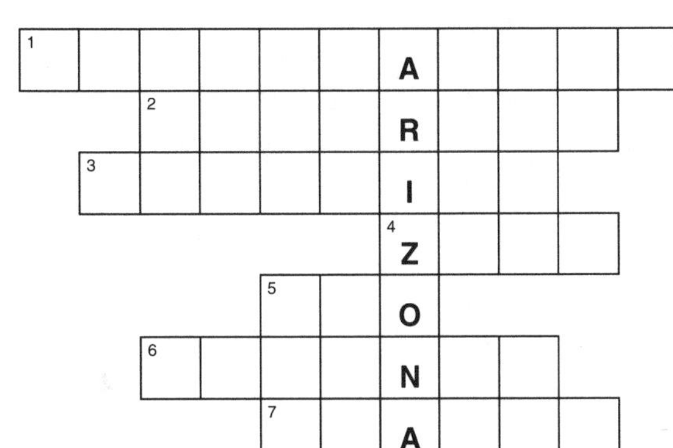

ACROSS:

1. Natural wonder of the world found in Arizona
2. Location of a famous gunfight in Arizona
3. Apache chief captured in 1886
4. Native Americans of Arizona
5. Location of Arizona's first copper mine
6. Capital city of Arizona
7. The oldest continuously occupied spot in the United States

62. COLORADO

C
O
L
O
R
A
D
O

ACROSS:

1. Mountains in Colorado
2. Home of the U.S. Air Force Academy
3. One of the nation's most famous winter resorts
4. 1859 gold rush slogan
5. The second American astronaut to orbit the earth
6. Famous anthem written in Colorado by Katherine Lee Bates
7. Capital city of Colorado
8. State flower of Colorado

Name ______________________________ Date ____________________

63. IDAHO

						1		I							
					2			D							
					3			A							
4								H							
					5			O							

ACROSS:

1. Capital city of Idaho
2. Popular mountain for skiers in Idaho
3. Idaho's most famous commodity
4. State tree of Idaho
5. Site of the first U.S. nuclear power plant

64. MONTANA

1							M									
2							O									
			3				N									
4							T									
		5					A									
		6					N									
					7		A									

ACROSS:

1. State bird of Montana
2. State flower of Montana
3. Capital city of Montana
4. First woman to serve in the U.S. House of Representatives
5. Nickname of Montana
6. Largest city in Montana
7. River in Montana

Name ______________________ Date ______________

65. NEVADA

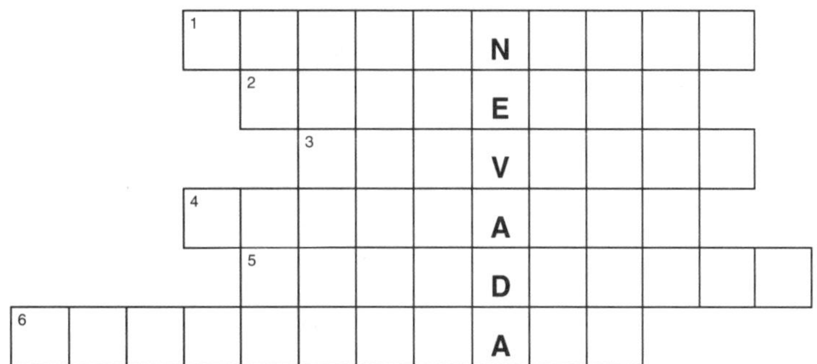

ACROSS: ______________________

1. Capital city of Nevada
2. The nation's gambling capital
3. The nation's marriage capital, with over fifty wedding chapels
4. Largest alpine lake in North America
5. Former name of Hoover Dam
6. Nickname of Nevada

Name ______________________ Date ______________

66. NEW MEXICO

ACROSS: ______________________

1. Capital city of New Mexico
2. Largest city in New Mexico
3. Mountain peak in northern New Mexico
4. Leading industry of New Mexico
5. Famous painter who derived inspiration from New Mexico's landscape
6. Namesake of New Mexico
7. "King of the Innkeepers" from New Mexico
8. Famous trapper, guide, and Indian agent
9. Site of the first atomic bomb test

Name ______________________ Date ______________

67. UTAH

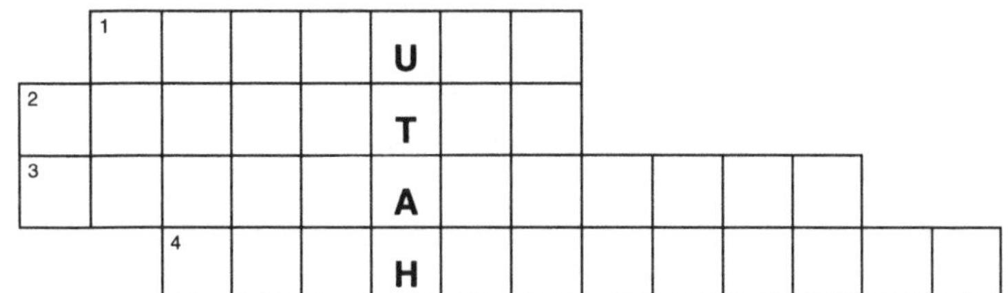

ACROSS: ______________________

1. State bird of Utah
2. State motto of Utah
3. Capital city of Utah
4. Nickname of Utah

68. WYOMING

1
W
2
Y
3
O
4
M
5
I
6
N
7
G

ACROSS: ______________________

1. World's first national park
2. Nation's first female governor
3. State tree of Wyoming
4. Famous mountain man of Wyoming
5. Famous geyser in Yellowstone National Park
6. Capital city of Wyoming
7. State motto of Wyoming

69. THE PACIFIC COAST STATES—I

ACROSS:

1. Nation's deepest lake
2. Tallest peak in the contiguous forty-eight states
3. Nickname of Washington
4. Pacific Coast's leading fishing port
5. U.S. president from California
6. Mountain range in California, Oregon, and Washington
7. Location of one of the world's most famous zoos
8. Nation's most populous state
9. Author of *The Grapes of Wrath*
10. Dam on the Columbia River, one of the world's largest producers of hydroelectric power
11. Radio and film star, famous for his "road comedies" with Bob Hope
12. Oregon's chief fishing port
13. Location of many California wineries
14. World War II general from California
15. Nickname of Oregon
16. Huge amusement park located at Anaheim
17. First American to climb Mt. Everest
18. Largest city in California
19. Location of a volcanic eruption in 1980
20. Famous landmark in Washington, built for the 1962 Century 21 Exposition
21. Nickname of California

Name ______________________ Date ______________

69. The Pacific Coast States—I

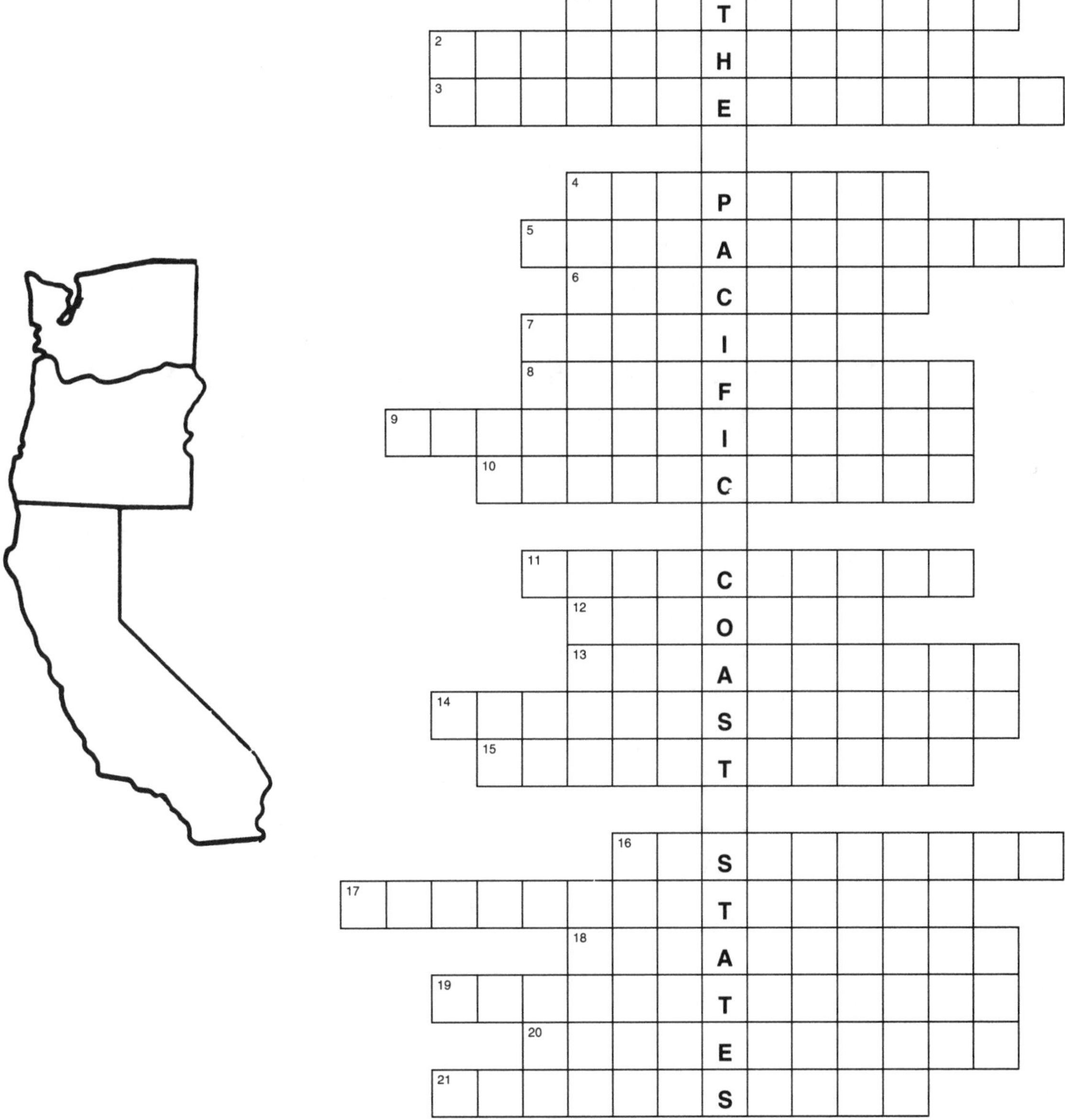

Name ______________________________ Date ____________________

70. THE PACIFIC COAST STATES—II

```
O F E U G E N E C S O S A L E M E C C E T
C U T O R E G O N A A R S H C D O O O S A
S P A L M S P R I N G S S S O N H T L O C
I R G E A P N P D A D I I O D R A W U J O
C S N E E N M I R N F E H O E G T Y M N M
N M E R T Y E E S D R T R B R O E Y B A A
A A D Y L G D A E R M A M A E L K R I S F
R D L O O W I L A E R I P U L D A S A R N
F A O A O O I N G A T E R A O I L O E O R
N T G O U O E L S S S E V U D A O S M E R
A M D Q W V F E L F K N O L P R N L I A D
S S E E A Y A F R A I A O P I O A N T N E
H S E D R T L U E U M G L S E S I C U A A
P H A B T M S L Q L O E E L R A H O O H T
O S U L E G T A O T S G T T R S S N N E H
R I E L I T O H H H W T T T I T O D O I V
T F A B A J I L N S A H M F E M T O G M A
L S H C N I L S D C T C A G O V E R E N L
A Q U A C U L T U R E M U L T I A S R N L
N M S I R U O T E N A P P L E S T L O A E
D N E W N F O R T Y N I N E R S A T L Y Y
S P O K A N E T R E S E D E V A J O M E I
S I E R R A C L U B O T N E M A R C A S Y
```

The following words are hidden in the puzzle. Words can be found horizontally, vertically, diagonally, and backward.

Death Valley
Puget Sound
Mojave Desert
Mt. Rainier
silver
San Francisco
aquaculture
Mt. Hood
Yosemite
apples
San Jose
Sierra Club
tourism

Willamette Valley
condor
Palm Springs
Salem
forty-niners
redwoods
Sierra Nevada
Hollywood
gold
Columbia
Fresno
Lake Tahoe
Portland

oil
San Joaquin Valley
whales
Spokane
Oregon
Mt. Shasta
copper
Anaheim
sequoias
Golden Gate
San Andreas Fault
timber
San Diego

Tacoma
Eureka
Mt. Adams
salmon
Olympia
cattle
Seattle
Big Sur
fish
Eugene
Sacramento
grapes

Name ______________________ Date ______________

71. CALIFORNIA

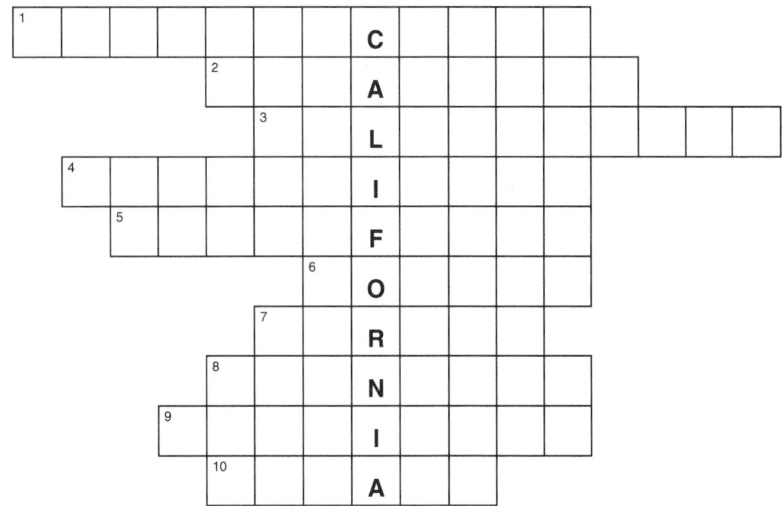

ACROSS:

1. Location of a terrible earthquake in 1906
2. Location of the legendary jumping–frog contest
3. Nickname of California
4. Nickname of the California gold rushers
5. Producer of the first film made in Hollywood, *In Old California*
6. North America's largest bird
7. State motto of California
8. Founder of the Sierra Club
9. Tallest peak in the contiguous United States
10. Desert in California

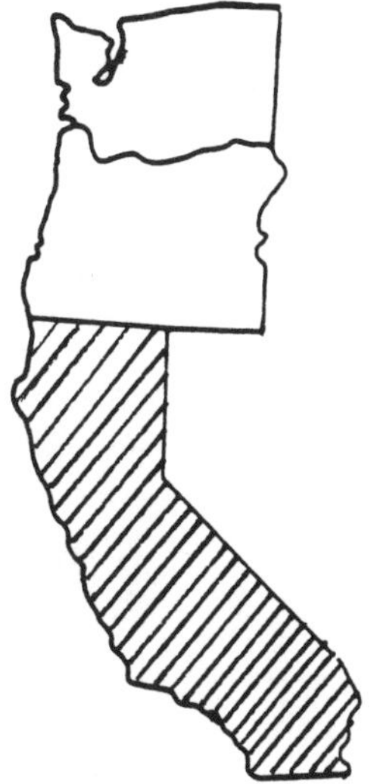

Name ______________________ Date ______________________

72. OREGON

ACROSS: ______________________

1. State flower of Oregon
2. Largest city in Oregon
3. Famous national park in Oregon
4. State tree of Oregon
5. River in Oregon
6. Nickname of Oregon

Name ______________________ Date ______________

73. WASHINGTON

1	W
2	A
3	S
4	H
5	I
6	N
7	G
8	T
9	O
10	N

ACROSS: ______________________________

1. First American to reach the top of Mt. Everest
2. River in Washington
3. Mountain range in Washington
4. Site of a volcanic eruption in 1980
5. River in Washington
6. Seattle's most famous landmark
7. Nickname of Washington
8. Largest city in Washington
9. Famous singer and actor from Washington
10. Dam on the Columbia River in Washington

74. ALASKA—I

ACROSS:

1. One of the leading industries in Alaska
2. Condition in which water below the tundra surface remains frozen throughout the year
3. Animal raised commercially for food and fur in Alaska
4. Northern point of the Trans-Alaska Pipeline
5. Alaska's mightiest river, flowing nearly two thousand miles
6. Industry in which Alaska leads the nation
7. Nickname of Alaska
8. State motto of Alaska
9. Sound where the largest oil spill in U.S. history occurred, in 1989
10. The highest peak in North America
11. Native Americans in Alaska
12. Southern point of the Trans-Alaska Pipeline
13. Capital city of Alaska
14. National park located in Alaska
15. Narrow body of water separating Alaska from Asia
16. Largest city in Alaska
17. Famous dogsled race held each March in Alaska
18. U.S. secretary of state who purchased Alaska from Russia in 1867
19. Islands off the southwestern coast of Alaska
20. Largest city in the interior of Alaska

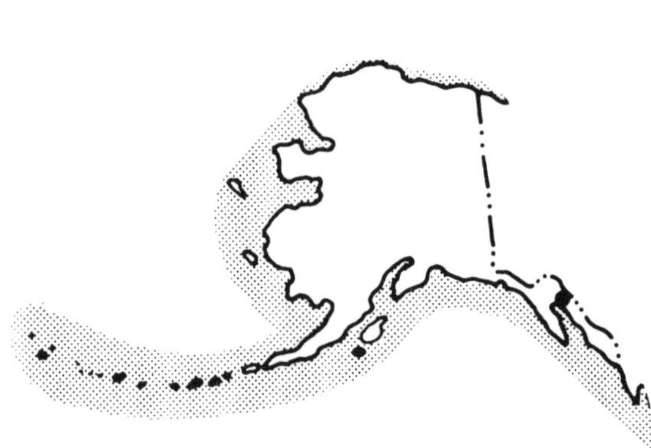

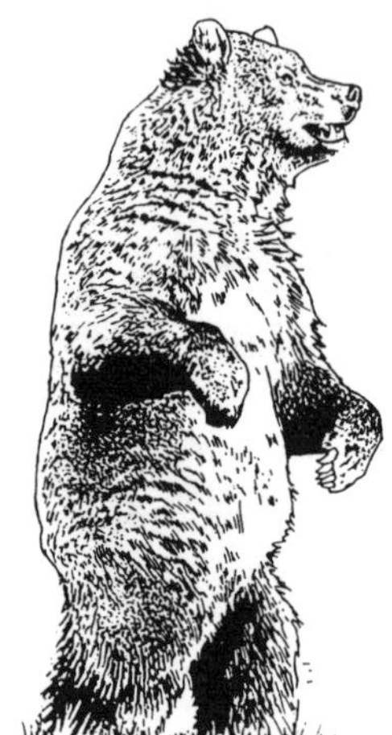

Name ______________________ Date ______________

74. Alaska—I

1 L
2 A
3 N
4 D
5 O
6 F
7 T
8 H
9 E
10 M
11 I
12 D
13 N
14 I
15 G
16 H
17 T
18 S
19 U
20 N

Name ______________________________ Date ____________________

75. ALASKA—II

```
W F H R E V I R A N A N A T E D E D M
U O B I R A C G L A C I E R N N N S O
S X G N P I N W A K S A L A I A K E O
T E S A C O O K I N L E T F L L U I S
H E L E L L L N C I L T U S E S S K E
K G A G V E O A O C S R I S P I K S R
O N E E A M P T R O S K O A I E O U E
D A S U L E U I R B A R T I P C K H P
I R S A T N C F H V E I E L T N W S P
A S S I D C A G I C M A A E O E I I O
K K N R I M N N O B R O R T U R M T C
I O A T R I U O E L C A S S R W R K P
S O C E N N C R A B D F N T I A I A A
L R P I E P O L S H T R O N S L V L N
A B M G R I Z Z L I E S W U M T E E H
N R E V I R E N I P U C R O P S R U A
D C H U K C H I S E A X S M E T O T N
I C E B E R G E M O N H W H A L E S D
U M A S U R L A W Y R T S E R O F N L
E V U A E N U J L E S K I M O S E N E
```

The following words are hidden in the puzzle. Words can be found horizontally, vertically, diagonally, and backward.

Arctic Circle
huskies
archipelago
fox
Cook Inlet
caribou
Kuskokwim River
mining
Eskimos
panhandle
seals
tin
Nome
snow
Tanana River
walrus
pipeline
Kodiak Island
Chukchi Sea
gold
crab
salmon
Alaska
eagles
North Slope
iceberg
Nunivak Island
oil
wolves
Sitka
moose
copper
lynx
permafrost
Mount St. Elias
glacier
Porcupine River
Juneau
totems
whales
timber
Brooks Range
forestry
grizzlies
Aleuts
tourism
polar bears
St. Lawrence Island
coal
tundra
furs

76. HAWAII—I

ACROSS:

1. Hawaii's second-largest crop
2. Wettest spot on earth, averaging more than 450 inches of rain a year
3. Hawaii's most important industry
4. Location of a U.S. naval base in Hawaii
5. Extinct volcano that is Hawaii's most familiar landmark
6. State flower of Hawaii
7. Pacific island region where Hawaii is located
8. European discoverer of the Hawaiian Islands, in 1778
9. Capital and largest city of Hawaii
10. Hawaii is the only state to produce this crop commercially
11. Rings of closely spaced, small coral islands
12. Most-populated of the Hawaiian Islands
13. Southernmost point of the United States, located on the Big Island
14. Native Hawaiian food made from the root of the taro plant
15. Largest mountain in the world, over ten thousand cubic miles
16. The major crop grown in Hawaii
17. Last monarch of Hawaii, author of "Aloha Oe"
18. Popular sport developed in Hawaii
19. Ship sunk by the Japanese on December 7, 1941
20. European name given to Hawaii in 1778

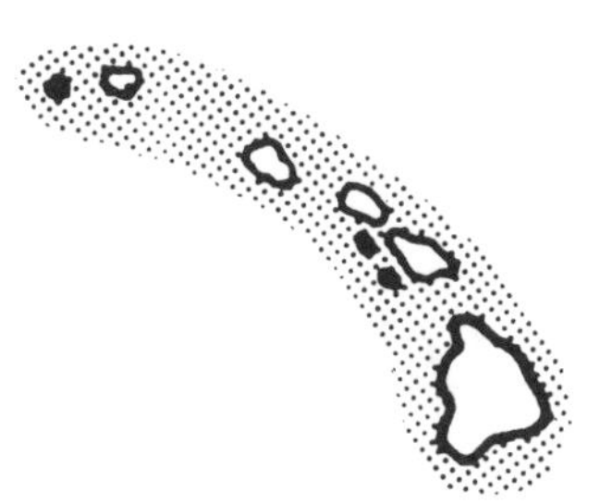

Name ______________________________ Date ______________________

76. Hawaii—I

1 . . . . . P . . . .
2 . . . . . A . . . .
3 . . R . . .
4 . . . . . A . . . .
5 . . . . . D . . . .
6 . . I . . . .
7 . . . . . S . .
8 . . E . . . . .
9 . . O . . . .
10 . . F . . . .
11 T . . . .
12 . H .
13 . . . E
14 P . .
15 . . . . A . . .
16 . . . . . C . . .
17 . . I . . . .
18 . . F . . .
19 . . . . . I . . . .
20 . . . . . . C . . . .

Name ______________________________ Date ____________________

77. HAWAII—II

```
I U A M S E L P P A E N I P K T M H I N
S U G A R C A N E Y L U A Y O L C O C A
L M S I R U O T I A A C A J N N P N L N
A A K S F J O A V H I B U H A O D O O A
N V A A E A K A I F A A A R C P H L R U
D A U O H O K I I M E D R E O A I U C E
S L L U L O N C U U A E R I A H A L H F
A I A O H M O A A E K U I I S L U U I A
H P M A A C N L C R O I N I T U A A D L
U E L U E A I O A L A O W A S A K A S L
L A I A H K R P D W O P A N K L H A M S
A R N H N A S R A N E V I A K E H S H D
W L L O L T O H E L C O K L O E A U A A
E H U L N U A C T E O A I A O W L R O E
E A A A O H A T I L F E K I L A E F L H
F R U L O T A U I A I S I S A R A I A D
F B L L E C A H L O A I B E U D K N N N
O O A N C S E L P B N O E N R R A G U O
C R G N I H S I F P A P A Y A S L U A M
S N O R K E L I N G O K C L N I A H M A
N O Y N A C A E M I A W H O G E M A U I
E N M T W A I A L E A L E P E L R O U D
```

The following words are hidden in the puzzle. Words can be found horizontally, vertically, diagonally, and backward.

aloha
volcanoes
Pearl Harbor
coral
luau
Pacific Ocean
pineapples
surfing
Kaula
Waimea Canyon
islands
Akaka Falls
coffee
Honolulu
Lanai
whales
Kohala
Mt. Waialeale
Diamond Head
Waikiki Beach
reefs
Maui
orchids
Maalaea Bay
leeward
snorkeling
plantation
Hanauma Bay
Polynesia
Molokai
Nanaue Falls
cattle
Haleakala
Mauna Loa
poi
Parker Ranch
Kahoolawe
papayas
atoll
Kona Coast
Kilauea
lava
Hilo
Mauna Kea
hula
Oahu
sugarcane
fishing
lei
Niihau
Koolau Range
Hawaii
tourism
Kauai

78. OUR NATION'S CAPITAL

The answers to the following clues are hidden in the puzzle. Circle the answer in the puzzle and then write the answer in the blank by the correct number. Answers can be found horizontally, vertically, diagonally, and backward.

1. African American who contributed to the design and construction of Washington, D.C.
2. State that donated the land for the nation's capital
3. President when the Capitol and White House were burned during the War of 1812
4. President who made the first television broadcast from the White House
5. Former name of the White House
6. First president to have a son born in the White House
7. River by which the capital was built
8. First president to die in office
9. City that served as the seat of government before Washington, D.C.
10. First Lady who hosted the first inaugural ball in Washington, D.C.
11. Second president to die in office
12. Country that destroyed much of the capital during the War of 1812
13. President both of whose daughters were married in the White House
14. What "D.C." in "Washington, D.C.," stands for
15. Person chosen by President Washington to design and oversee the planning of the capital
16. Constitutional amendment that allows residents of Washington, D.C., to vote in presidential elections
17. First president to have a son married in the White House
18. Name for the building where Congress meets
19. Only president who did not live in the White House
20. First president to have a daughter married in the White House
21. Practice that was outlawed in Washington, D.C., by the Compromise of 1850
22. First Lady who died in the White House
23. City that served as the seat of government when the Constitution was written
24. First president inaugurated in Washington, D.C.
25. President who was shot and wounded in Washington, D.C., in an unsuccessful assassination attempt
26. First president to live in the White House
27. First president to be assassinated in Washington, D.C.
28. Person chosen by President Washington to survey and map out the boundaries of the capital
29. Second president to be assassinated in Washington, D.C.
30. First Lady who hung her laundry in the East Room of the newly constructed White House

Name ______________________________ Date ____________________

78. Our Nation's Capital

T D S Y D S R M K W H M G M P L S D A C C A
M I C N L R I C H A R D N I X O N B G J P M
A N D R E W E L L I C O T T H A R L O T W D
F M T R I X H J D P S P V N L A G E B H I R
L B E F F S E G E I H D K Y H E D E T S L I
E M N J R E C C D F B N R A O A P O T M L H
B A O A A S A A U A W A M R R D C R C A I T
E S S M G J M G C T M L G T O P I N E D A Y
F R I E S S O A M F I E E L L C C O K A M T
C W R S E A T M D N W V L J T S T M A N H N
R J R M M B O J C A A E E O F N J S A H E E
R H A O A A P O S L Y L F M A H D E J O N W
B J H N J B L H S M M C A F A C D M B J R T
S J E R G N I L A L O R N W M N B A D P Y N
C R N O J N J D E L Y E Y I A S S J H F H O
G A I E G R I Y U L L V N L U M E I E R A S
D H L T A S M M A E E O Y A A Q L D O R R R
L S O W O E B N R E T R J D I A N N M N R E
D N R N U I D R N K A G A L D A A H A P I F
H O A O A K E D R M O L N E L L T H O E S F
U N C A P I T O L H I L L G D I T E D J O E
S T A T P E Y S R A E P N R A D Y T O U N J
S K R O Y W E N G E H E E D A R T E V A L S
P U Z A E D A I E I H A R R Y T R U M A N A
I O Y N U D B U A M G M I E S R O B R I C M
N R O L Y A T Y R A H C A Z I X I D G J M O
K B E N J A M I N B A N N E K E R R J B R H
F C D E N B O T C C B M J N O S R M E O H T

1. ____________________
2. ____________________
3. ____________________
4. ____________________
5. ____________________
6. ____________________
7. ____________________
8. ____________________
9. ____________________
10. ____________________
11. ____________________
12. ____________________
13. ____________________
14. ____________________
15. ____________________
16. ____________________
17. ____________________
18. ____________________
19. ____________________
20. ____________________
21. ____________________
22. ____________________
23. ____________________
24. ____________________
25. ____________________
26. ____________________
27. ____________________
28. ____________________
29. ____________________
30. ____________________

79. FAMOUS CITIES IN THE UNITED STATES—I

ACROSS:

1. Location of the nation's tallest monument, the Gateway Arch
3. City that was burned during General Sherman's "March to the Sea"
4. Nation's automotive capital
5. Location of Touro Synagogue, the country's oldest Jewish house of worship
8. Location of the nation's first national historical park, where Washington's army camped during the winter of 1776–77
9. Site of Arizona's first copper mine, in 1854
12. City where a famous civil rights march began, led by Martin Luther King, Jr.
13. Original capital of the Confederacy
16. Site of the first organized baseball game in 1846
17. Alaska's largest city
19. "The Pittsburgh of the South"
21. City that hosted the first baseball World Series in 1903
22. Arkansas' largest city
28. Location of the National Baseball Hall of Fame
29. "The Athens of the South"
31. "The onion-growing capital of the world"
33. Site of the assassination of Martin Luther King, Jr.
36. Hometown of Samuel Clemens (Mark Twain)
37. Site of the assassination of President McKinley
38. City where Harriet Beecher Stowe wrote *Uncle Tom's Cabin*
39. Location of the *Hindenburg* crash in 1937
40. Southernmost city in the continental United States
41. Nation's gambling capital

DOWN:

1. Oldest capital city in the United States, originally founded by the Spanish in 1610, and also the highest, at almost seven thousand feet
2. Site of the first U.S. nuclear power plant in 1955
6. The leading meat-packing city in the United States
7. Smallest capital city in the nation
10. Nation's oldest city
11. Site of the first intercollegiate football game in 1869
14. Capital of the Confederate States of America
15. Site of a famous gunfight, at the O.K. Corral
18. Original movie capital of the nation
20. City where gold was discovered in 1899
23. Site of the annual Miss America Pageant
24. Location of the U.S. Naval Academy
25. Site of a famous school founded by Booker T. Washington in 1881
26. Burial site of President Eisenhower
27. Site of the "World's Largest Fish Fry," an annual festival held in Tennessee
30. Site of an important Civil War battle, giving Union forces control of the Mississippi River
32. "The Insurance Capital of the World"
34. One of the world's greatest steel centers
35. Site of the assassination of President Kennedy

Name ______________________ Date ______________________

79. Famous Cities in the United States—I

1 2 3 4 5 6 7 8 9 10 11 12 13 14 15 16 17 18 19 20 21 22 23 24 25 26 27 28 29 30 31 32 33 34 35 36 37 38 39 40 41

80. FAMOUS CITIES IN THE UNITED STATES—II

ACROSS: ______

1. Site of the only diamonds ever mined in the United States
5. California's largest city
6. Location of one of the world's largest aluminum plants
10. Location of the world's leading producer of breakfast cereals
11. Site of the famous "Monkey Trial" in 1925
12. Location of the world's tallest building, the Sears Tower
13. Location of Thomas Edison's laboratory
15. "The Chemical Capital of the World," Delaware's largest city
17. This Georgia city boasts more cherry trees than any other U.S. city
18. Location of the London Bridge
19. City where Mormon founder Joseph Smith was killed
20. Site of the oldest continuously run horse race in the nation
25. Site of the atomic energy research plant built in 1942
26. City where basketball was invented by Dr. James Naismith in 1891
27. City at the western end of the Erie Canal
28. Location of the headquarters of NASA's spacecraft projects
29. Location of the U.S. Coast Guard Academy
30. Site of the nation's first commercial oil well, drilled in 1859
31. Location of the "Little White House," where President Franklin D. Roosevelt died
32. Site of one of the Civil War's bloodiest battles and Lincoln's most-famous speech

DOWN: ______

2. Location of Boys Town, a community of homeless and underprivileged children, founded by Father Flanagan in 1917
3. City where the nation's first subway system opened, in 1897
4. Hometown of President Clinton
7. Site of America's first law school, established by Tapping Reeve in 1784
8. Home of the world's first professional baseball team, the Red Stockings
9. "The Birthplace of Jazz"
10. Location of the largest oil refinery in the United States
11. Westernmost Atlantic port
14. Burial site of Presidents Monroe and Tyler
16. Location of the nation's leading producer of rubber
19. Location of Yale University
21. Site of America's first victory in the Revolutionary War
22. Ohio's largest city
23. Site where the first shots were fired in the Revolutionary War
24. The nation's largest popcorn plant is located in this Iowa city

Name ______________________ Date ______________

80. Famous Cities in the United States—II

81. RIVERS OF THE UNITED STATES—I

Identify the state by its rivers.

ACROSS: ______________________________

1. Apalachicola, St. Johns, and Suwannee
2. Columbia, Snake, and Yakima
3. Allegheny, Delaware, and Susquehanna
4. Columbia, Snake, and Willamette
5. Delaware, Hudson, and Raritan
6. Blackstone, Pawtuxet, and Seekonk
7. Altamaha, Chattahoochee, and Savannah
8. Klamath, Sacramento, and San Joaquin
9. Green, Kentucky, and Ohio
10. Androscoggin, Connecticut, and Merrimack
11. Pecos, Rio Grande, and San Juan
12. Charles, Connecticut, and Merrimack
13. Kootenai, Missouri, and Yellowstone
14. Grand, Kalamazoo, and Saginaw
15. Housatonic, Naugatuck, and Thames
16. Cumberland, Holston, and Mississippi
17. Little Missouri, Missouri, and Sheyenne
18. Grand, Mississippi, and Osage
19. Bear, Colorado, and Green
20. Mississippi, Red, and White
21. Brazos, Rio Grande, and Sabine
22. Kennebec, Penobscot, and St. Croix
23. Minnesota, Mississippi, and St. Croix

Name ______________________ Date ______________

81. Rivers of the United States—I

1 R
2 I
3 V
4 E
5 R
6 S

7 O
8 F

9 T
10 H
11 E

12 U
13 N
14 I
15 T
16 E
17 D

18 S
19 T
20 A
21 T
22 E
23 S

82. RIVERS OF THE UNITED STATES—II

Identify the state by its rivers.

ACROSS: ______________________________

1. Patuxent, Potomac, and Susquehanna
2. Ohio, Wabash, and White
3. Colorado, Humboldt, and Truckee
4. Connecticut, White, and Winooski
5. North Platte, Platte, and South Platte
6. Atchafalaya, Mississippi, and Red
7. Colorado, Gila, and Little Colorado
8. Klamath, Sacramento, and San Joaquin
9. Monongahela, Ohio, and Potomac
10. Arkansas, Cimarron, and Red
11. Hudson, Mohawk, and St. Lawrence
12. Cheyenne, James, and Missouri
13. Arkansas, Kansas, and Missouri
14. James, Potomac, and York
15. Cape Fear, Pee Dee, and Roanoke
16. Christina, Delaware, and Nanticoke
17. Clearwater, Salmon, and Snake
18. Kuskokwim, Tanana, and Yukon
19. Trinity, Colorado, and White
20. Ashley, Great Pee Dee, and Savannah
21. Sevier, Bear, and Virgin
22. Passaic, Raritan, and Delaware
23. Chippewa, St. Croix, and Wisconsin

Name ______________________ Date ______________

82. Rivers of the United States—II

1		R												
2		I												
3		V												
4		E												
5		R												
6		S												
7		O												
8		F												
9		T												
10		H												
11		E												
12		U												
13		N												
14		I												
15		T												
16		E												
17		D												
18		S												
19		T												
20		A												
21		T												
22		E												
23		S												

83. LAKES AND BODIES OF WATER IN THE UNITED STATES

ACROSS:

2. Lake in western Tennessee
5. Bay in western Florida
7. Smallest of the Great Lakes
10. Bay in eastern New Jersey
12. Bay in eastern Massachusetts
13. Bay in southern Louisiana
14. Lake created by Hoover Dam
15. Second-largest natural freshwater body entirely within the United States
21. Second smallest of the Great Lakes
22. Lake on the border of South Dakota and Minnesota
24. Nation's deepest lake
25. Lake created by the first dam built by the Tennessee Valley Authority, named after the Nebraska senator who proposed the project
28. Sound in western Washington
29. Sound in southern Massachusetts
30. Lake in central South Dakota
32. Lake in southern Utah
34. Famous pond where Henry David Thoreau lived alone
35. Largest natural freshwater lake west of the Mississippi River
37. Third largest of the Great Lakes
38. Largest of the Great Lakes
39. Bay north of Alaska, where oil was discovered in 1968

DOWN:

1. Lake in eastern Wisconsin
3. Famous canal in New York
4. Bay between the Hawaiian islands of Maui and Kahoolawe
5. Lake on the border of Texas and Oklahoma
6. Lake on the border of New York and Vermont
8. Bay between Maryland and Virginia, one of the nation's most bountiful sources of seafood
9. Popular resort area in New York, famous for its mineral baths
11. Lake on the border of California and Nevada
14. Bay in southern Alabama
16. Lake in northern Oklahoma
17. Country's first national preserve, a fashionable spa in Arkansas
18. Bay in eastern Michigan
19. Lake that has a higher saline content than either the Atlantic or Pacific oceans
20. Largest lake in New Hampshire
23. Lake in western Maine
26. Lake where the London Bridge is located
27. Second largest of the Great Lakes
28. Lake in northern New York, site of the 1980 Winter Olympics
31. Bay in eastern Wisconsin
33. Sound in eastern North Carolina
36. Largest alpine lake in North America

Name ______________________ Date ______________

83. Lakes and Bodies of Water in the United States

84. MOUNTAINS AND RIVERS OF THE UNITED STATES

ACROSS:

2. Mountains in New Mexico
6. River separating Oregon and Washington
7. Mountains in New Hampshire
9. River in Texas
13. Mountains in Nevada
15. River in Connecticut
18. Mountains in southern New York
20. River in southern Nebraska
23. River in southwestern Ohio
24. River and mountains in Pennsylvania
25. River in western Mississippi
28. Mountains in southwestern Oklahoma
31. River in southeastern Pennsylvania and northern Maryland
32. River in southwestern Pennsylvania
34. River in eastern North Carolina
38. River in southern Mississippi
39. River in southeastern Utah
40. Mountain in southeastern Kentucky
41. River in western Florida
43. River separating Texas and Oklahoma
44. River in Virginia and North Carolina
47. River in western Missouri
50. River separating Oregon and Idaho
51. River in Alaska
53. River in southeastern Washington
54. River in eastern Massachusetts
55. River in southeastern Michigan
57. Mountain range in the eastern United States
59. River in southern Montana and northern Wyoming
61. "Hills" in the lower part of Mississippi
62. River in western Massachusetts and central Connecticut
63. Mountains in western Montana
64. River flowing through the Grand Canyon

DOWN:

1. River in eastern Virginia
2. River in eastern South Dakota
3. River in central West Virginia
4. River separating Kentucky and Indiana
5. River in southwestern Oregon
8. River in western Nevada
9. "Mountains" in southwestern South Dakota
10. River in central Vermont
11. Mountains in California, Oregon, and Washington
12. Mountains in eastern Tennessee
14. River in southern Montana
16. Mountains in western Virginia and North Carolina
17. River in North Dakota
19. Mountains in northern New York
21. River in California
22. Mountains in northwestern Arkansas
26. River separating Iowa and Nebraska
27. River separating Pennsylvania and New Jersey
29. River in eastern New York
30. River in Kansas and Oklahoma
33. River separating Georgia and South Carolina
35. Mountains in southern Vermont
36. River in western Wisconsin
37. River in central Virginia
38. River in eastern New Mexico
42. River in Idaho
44. River separating Texas and Mexico
45. River in North and South Dakota
46. River separating southern Illinois and Indiana
48. River in central Rhode Island
49. River in eastern South Carolina
52. River in southern Michigan
56. River in southern Alabama
58. River in New Mexico
60. River in southern Arizona

Name ____________________ Date ____________________

84. Mountains and Rivers of the United States

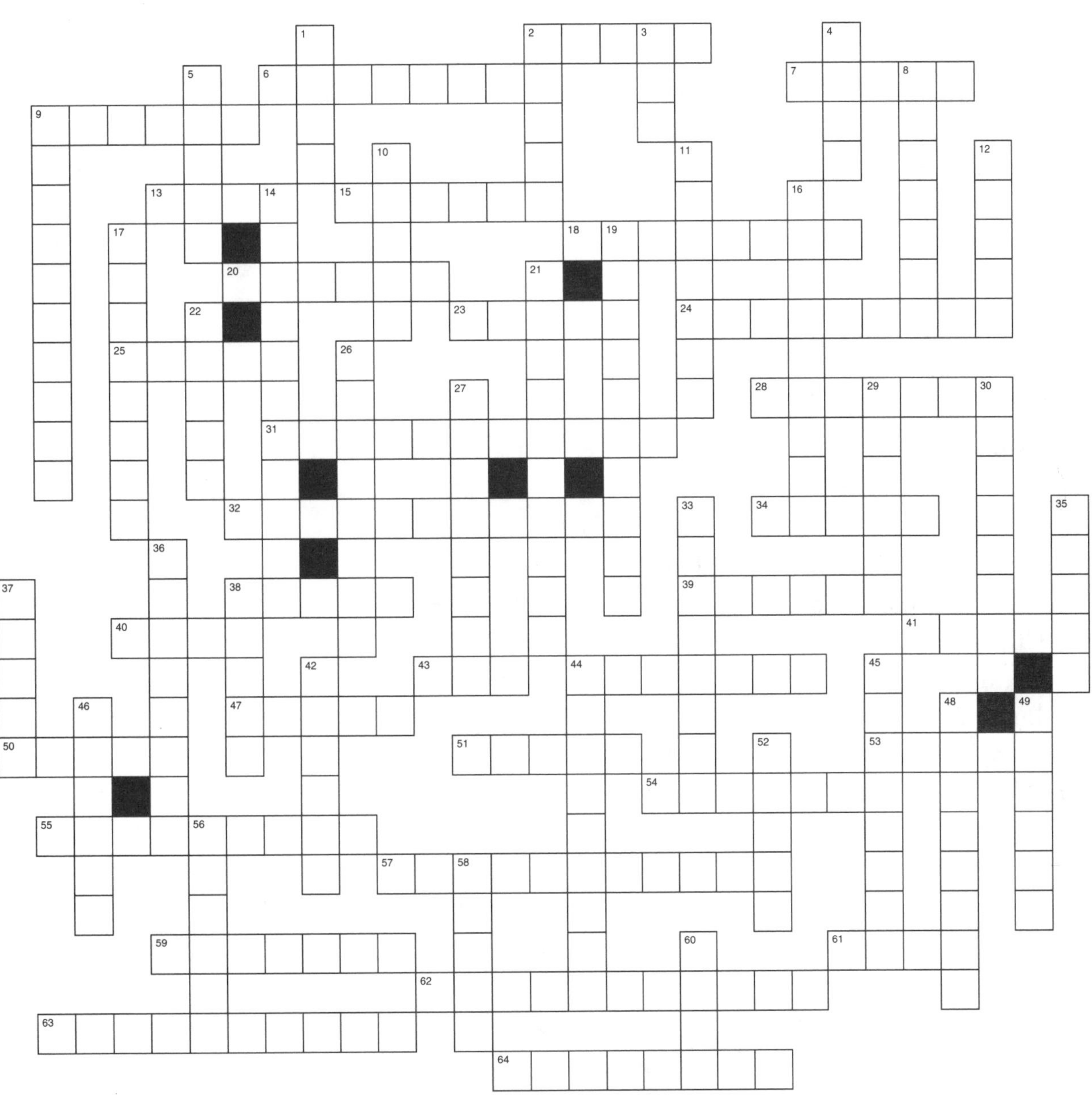

85. HIGH POINTS OF THE UNITED STATES

Identify the state by its highest point of elevation.

ACROSS: ____________________

2. Boundary Peak 13,140′
4. Black Mesa 4,973′
6. Humphrey's Peak 12,633′
12. Jerimoth Hill 812′
13. Borah Peak 12,662′
16. Mt. Whitney 14,494′
17. Kings Peak 13,528′
19. Mt. Washington 6,288′
22. Gannett Peak 13,804′
23. Granite Peak 12,799′
24. Guadalupe Peak 8,749′
27. Mt. Curwood 1,980′
28. Mt. Katahdin 5,268′
29. Mt. Mitchell 6,684′
30. Mt. Sunflower 4,039′

DOWN: ____________________

1. Brasstown Bald 4,784′
3. Cheaha Mountain 2,407′
5. Mt. Greylock 3,491′
7. Mt. Hood 11,239′
8. Magazine Mountain 2,753′
9. Clingman's Dome 6,643′
10. Backbone Mountain 3,360′
11. Borah Peak 12,662′
14. Campbell Hill 1,550′
15. Mt. Rainier 14,410′
16. Mt. Frissel 2,380′
18. Mt. Elbert 14,433′
20. Mauna Kea 13,796′
21. Charles Mound 1,235′
25. Mt. McKinley 20,320′
26. Campbell Hill 1,550′

Name ______________________ Date ______________

85. High Points of the United States

86. ISLANDS OF THE UNITED STATES

The names of the following islands are hidden in the puzzle. Circle the name of the island in the puzzle and in the blank beside it write the name of the state where it is located. Names can be found horizontally, vertically, diagonally, and backward.

Manhattan	________________	Maui	________________
St. Lawrence	________________	Kodiak	________________
Key West	________________	Pecan	________________
Jekyll	________________	Santa Catalina	________________
Avery	________________	Martha's Vineyard	________________
Assateague	________________	Hilton Head	________________
Madeline	________________	Simons	________________
Molokai	________________	Chincoteague	________________
Prudence	________________	Aquidneck	________________
Padre	________________	Kauai	________________
Captiva	________________	Key Largo	________________
Channel	________________	Apostle	________________
Mackinac	________________	Long	________________
Queen Charlotte	________________	Tybee	________________
Mt. Desert	________________	Pea	________________
Lanai	________________	Aleutian	________________
Bois Blanc	________________	Washington	________________
Wassaw	________________	Kahoolawe	________________
Nunivak	________________	Sanibel	________________
Fire	________________	Beaver	________________
Nantucket	________________	North Manitou	________________
Key Biscayne	________________	San Clemente	________________
Parris	________________	Niihau	________________
Roanoke	________________	Bodie	________________
Oahu	________________	Ellis	________________

Name ______________________ Date ______________

86. Islands in the United States

```
A E U G A E T O C N I H C T M L C R K M
E H I L T O N H E A D S I R R A P J A A
N K E Y W E S T P M D L M O L O K A I C
A E U G A E T A S S A D A A A B J E D K
T B O S S A R T E K C U T N A N F K O I
T A G E H R L I E R I F I O A I O N K N
A M R N I Y J E K Y L L M K R I E O A A
H U A S N R B U U P A D R E L K H R E C
N M L R G Y H K A T M T D E S E R T T G
A P Y G T A A S A N I B E L N Y R H T D
M G E O O H V C R H W A S S A W E M O A
A G K A N S A E G N O L N E C E N A L Q
R P J O U T V S R N B O D I E S Y N R U
I R E S N L I H V Y M A L N P T A I A I
W U E A I A T B O I S B L A N C C T H D
E D S V V W P T S U N K L E W W S O C N
S E L E A R A Y M A D E L I N E I U N E
O N A R K E C B P M N L Y I P A B L E C
T C N Y L N B E L N I I H A U I Y U E K
M E A L A C A E A S M S D A R J E H U R
U B I O B E D H Y C H R K W T D K A Q O
A S Y S A N C L E M E N T E L T S O P A
```

87. STATE NAME ORIGINS

ACROSS:

1. Spanish for "red"
3. Chippewa for "great river"
6. Spanish for "mountainous"
8. Algonquin name for "muddy water"
12. Spanish for "snow-clad"
13. Honors King Louis XIV of France
14. Honors the first president of the United States
17. Honors King Charles I of England
21. Named after the former French province of Mayne
23. Sioux for "beautiful land"
24. Algonquin for "large mountain place"
25. Russian version of the Aleut word meaning "great land"
27. Named from the French words meaning "green mountain"
31. Navajo for "higher up"
32. Algonquin for "beside the long river"
34. Land of the Indians
35. Honors Admiral William Penn, father of the state's founder
36. Shoshone word for "beautiful water"
37. Sioux for "friend" or "ally"
38. Algonquin for "men" or "warriors"
39. Mythical island paradise in Spanish literature
44. Honors Queen Henrietta Marie of England
45. Choctaw for "red people"
46. Perhaps named from the French word "ouragan," an early name for the Columbia River
47. Named after the Aztec war god Mexitil

DOWN:

2. Iroquois for "beautiful river"
4. From "ayuxowu;" Sioux word for "beautiful land" or "this is the place"
5. Spanish for "feast of flowers"
7. Caddo for "friendly tribe"
9. Shoshone for "salmon tribe;" a possible source for this state's name
10. Indian tribe of the Creek confederacy
11. Omaha for "broad river"
12. Honors the British Duke of York
15. Honors King George II of England
16. Chippewa for "grassy place"
17. Named after the British county of Hampshire
18. Cherokee for "villages on the river"
19. French version of "Kansas"
20. Spanish version of the Pima word meaning "little spring place"
22. Iroquois for "meadowland"
26. Honors King Charles I of England
28. Sioux for "south wind people"
29. Named after the Greek island of Rhodes
30. Honors Queen Elizabeth I of England, the "Virgin Queen"
33. Polynesian word for "homeland"
40. Thought to be an invented word, coined to sound Indian
41. Iroquois for "great river"
42. Sioux for "this is the place"
43. Shoshone for "light on the mountains"

Name ______________________ Date ______________

87. State Name Origins

88. STATE NICKNAMES—I

ACROSS:

1. The Lumber State
2. The Empire State
7. The Volunteer State
8. The Border State
9. The Green Mountain State
12. The Land of Lincoln
13. The Grand Canyon State
14. The Sunshine State
15. The Prairie State
16. The Last Frontier
17. The Gem State
20. The Granite State
22. The Silver State
24. The Buckeye State
25. The Great Land
26. The Pine Tree State

28. The Gateway State
30. The Corn State
32. The Jayhawker State
33. Mother of the West
34. The Centennial State
36. The Beehive State
39. The Big Sky Country
40. The Magnolia State
41. The Bayou State
45. The Evergreen State
47. The Hawkeye State
48. The Beaver State
49. The Aloha State
50. The Mormon State
51. The Border State
52. Land of the Saints

DOWN:

1. The Mudcat State
2. The Mining State
3. The Quaker State
4. The Show Me State
5. The Antelope State
6. The Highest State
10. The Cornhusker State
11. The Cavalier State
12. The Hoosier State
18. The Pineapple State
19. The Land of Enchantment
21. The Cowboy State
23. The Golden State
27. The Badger State
28. Heartland of the Nation
29. Paradise of the Pacific
31. The Pelican State
35. The Sooner State
37. The Wolverine State
38. The Old Dominion
42. The Sunset State
43. Gem of the Mountains
44. Land of the Midnight Sun
46. Land Where the Tall Corn Grows

Name ______________________ Date ______________

88. State Nicknames—I

89. STATE NICKNAMES—II

ACROSS:

3. The Tobacco State
4. The Palmetto State
5. The Corn State
7. America's Dairyland
9. The Baked Bean State
11. The Cave State
12. Land of Infinite Variety
16. The Boomer State
19. The Excelsior State
20. The Nation's Breadbasket
21. Land of the Shining Mountains
25. The Smallest State
26. The Salt Lake State
29. The Mother of Presidents
30. The Constitution State
33. The Hawkeye State
34. The Sugar State
36. The Auto State
37. The Rocky Mountain State
39. Land Where the Tall Corn Grows
42. The Heart of Dixie
43. The Breadbasket of America
44. The Lone Star State
46. The Valentine State
47. The Grand Canyon State
49. The Peach State
50. The Pine Tree State
51. The First State
55. The Land of Opportunity
56. The Keystone State
57. The Buckeye State
59. The Lead State
60. The Tarheel State
62. The Bay State
64. The Gateway State
65. The Treasure State
66. The Lumber State
67. The Orange State
69. The Hawkeye State
70. The Blizzard State
71. The Ocean State
72. The North Star State

DOWN:

1. The Cyclone State
2. The Pine Tree State
3. The Squatter State
6. Heartland of the Nation
8. The Corn State
10. Pacific Wonderland
13. The Mormon State
14. The Bluegrass State
15. The Rice State
17. The Old Colony State
18. Land of Steady Habits
19. The White Mountain State
22. The Spanish State
23. Switzerland of America
24. The Equality State
27. Mother of Presidents
28. The Old North State
31. The Big Bend State
32. The Nation's Breadbasket
35. The Gopher State
38. The Diamond State
40. The Natural State
41. The Alligator State
42. The Yellowhammer State
45. The Webfoot State
48. The Mountain State
52. The Sunflower State
53. The Peninsula State
54. The Bread and Butter State
58. The Free State
61. The Goober State
63. Land of the Midnight Sun
68. The Corn State

Name ______________________ Date ______________

89. State Nicknames—II

90. STATE CAPITALS

ACROSS: ______

3. Capital of Iowa
5. Capital of Idaho
7. Capital of Washington
10. Capital of Virginia
12. Capital of Massachusetts
15. Capital of Delaware
16. Capital of Mississippi
18. Capital of Georgia
19. Capital of Texas
21. Capital of Colorado
22. Capital of Florida
26. Capital of Ohio
28. Capital of New Mexico
30. Capital of Arkansas
34. Capital of North Carolina
36. Capital of Oklahoma
37. Capital of Kansas
38. Capital of Missouri
39. Capital of Maine
40. Capital of California
41. Capital of Wyoming
42. Capital of Oregon

DOWN: ______

1. Capital of South Carolina
2. Capital of New Jersey
4. Capital of Illinois
5. Capital of Louisiana
6. Capital of Pennsylvania
8. Capital of Rhode Island
9. Capital of Hawaii
11. Capital of Indiana
13. Capital of Wisconsin
14. Capital of Alaska
17. Capital of Connecticut
20. Capital of North Dakota
23. Capital of Montana
24. Capital of Maine
25. Capital of South Dakota
27. Capital of Alabama
29. Capital of New York
31. Capital of Michigan
32. Capital of Arizona
33. Capital of Nebraska
35. Capital of Minnesota

☆☆☆☆☆☆☆☆☆☆☆☆☆

Name ______________________________ Date ____________________

90. State Capitals

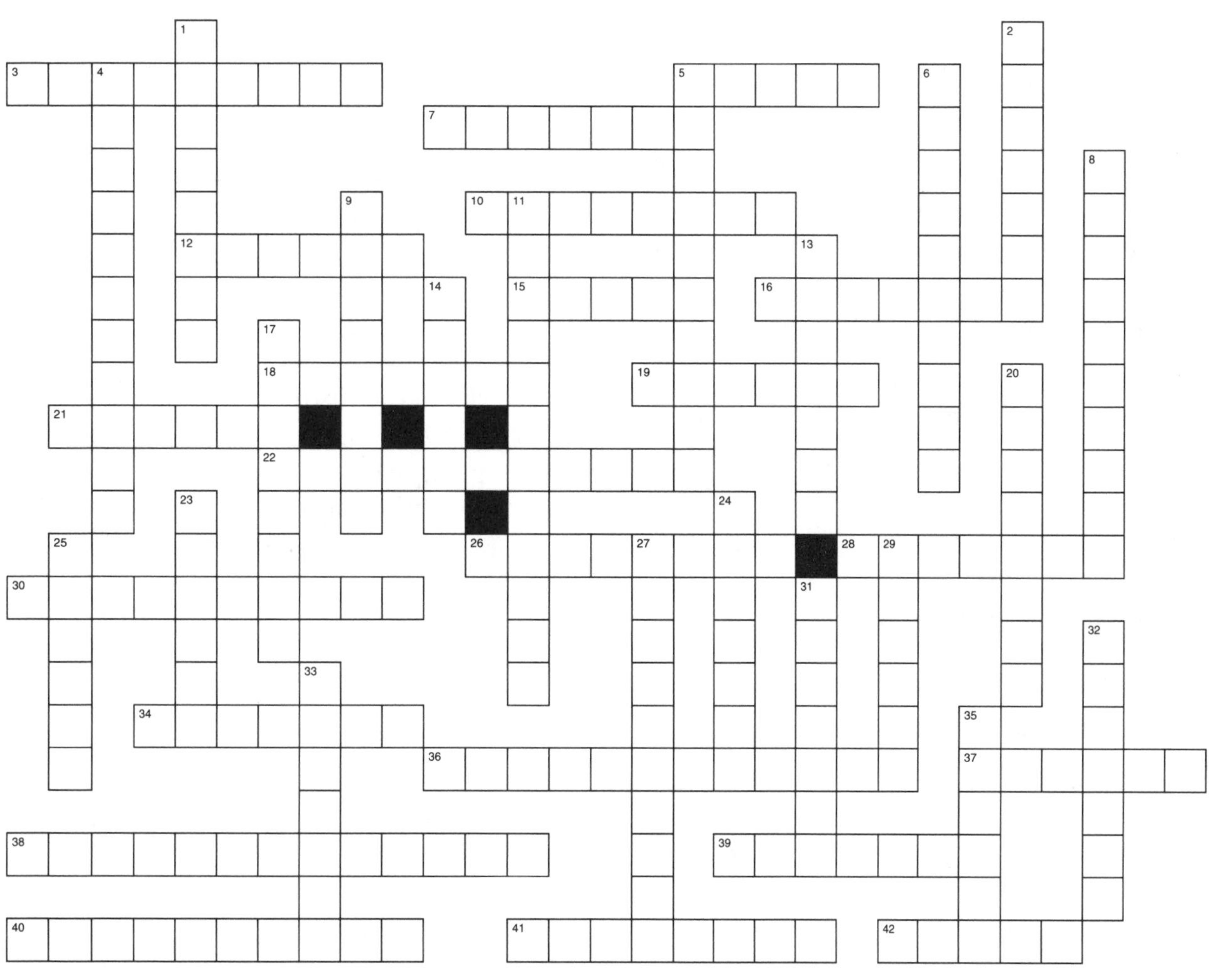

91. STATE MOTTOES

ACROSS:

3. Under God, the People Rule
4. Wisdom, Justice, and Moderation
7. With God, All Things Are Possible
9. Live Free or Die
12. Friendship
14. Virtute et Armis (By Valor and Arms)
17. Alis Volat Propiis (She Flies with Her Own Wings)
18. With God, All Things Are Possible
20. Agriculture and Commerce
22. State Sovereignty—National Union
23. With God, All Things Are Possible
25. Excelsior (Ever Upward)
28. Our Liberties We Prize, and Our Rights We Will Maintain
29. L'Etoile du Nord (Star of the North)
31. Audemus Jura Nostra Defendere (We Dare Defend Our Rights)
33. With God, All Things Are Possible
35. Union, Justice, Confidence
38. In God We Trust
40. Eureka! (I Have Found It)
42. Regnat Populus (The People Rule)
47. The Crossroads of America
48. All for Our Country
49. Friendship
51. North to the Future
52. Ense Petit Placidam sub Libertate Quietem (By the Sword We Seek Peace, but Peace Only Under Liberty)
53. Liberty and Prosperity
54. Nil Sine Numine (Nothing Without Providence)

DOWN:

1. Esto Perpetua (Let It Be Perpetual)
2. Our Liberties We Prize, and Our Rights We Will Maintain
5. Alis Volat Propiis (She Flies with Her Own Wings)
6. Industry
8. With God, All Things Are Possible
10. Dirigo (I Direct)
11. Freedom and Unity
13. Liberty and Union, Now and Forever, One and Inseparable
14. Salus Populi Suprema Lex Esto (The Welfare of the People Shall be the Supreme Law)
15. Our Liberties We Prize, and Our Rights We Will Maintain
16. Virtue, Liberty, and Independence
19. Montani Semper Liberi (Mountains Are Always Free)
21. Sic Semper Tyrannis (Thus Always to Tyrants)
24. Dirigo (I Direct)
26. Crescit Eundo (It Grows as It Goes)
27. Fatti Maschii, Parole Femine (Manly Deeds, Womanly Words)
29. Dirigo (I Direct)
30. Labor Omnia Vincit (Labor Conquers All Things)
32. Ditat Deus (God Enriches)
34. State Sovereignty—National Union
36. Ad Astra per Aspera (To the Stars Through Difficulties)
37. Alki (By and By)
39. North to the Future
41. Liberty and Independence
43. United We Stand, Divided We Fall
44. Industry
45. Dirigo (I Direct)
46. Ua Mau ke Ea o ka Aina i ka Pono (The Life of the Land Is Perpetuated in Righteousness)
50. Esto Perpetua (Let It Be Perpetual)

Name ______________________ Date ______________

91. State Mottoes

92. STATE BIRDS

ACROSS:

7. State bird of Alabama
9. State bird of South Dakota
10. State bird of Louisiana
11. State bird of Iowa, New Jersey, and Washington
12. State bird of Minnesota
14. State bird of Alaska
15. State bird of Connecticut
16. State bird of New Mexico
21. State bird of Kansas, Montana, and North Dakota
22. State bird of Utah
24. State bird of Maine and Massachusetts
26. State bird of Pennsylvania
28. State bird of Virginia and North Carolina
29. State bird of Michigan
30. State bird of Wisconsin
32. State bird of Idaho and Missouri
33. State bird of Delaware

DOWN:

1. State bird of Arizona
2. State bird of Louisiana
3. State bird of California
4. State bird of Minnesota
5. State bird of Vermont
6. State bird of Kentucky, West Virginia, and Indiana
8. State bird of Oregon, Nebraska, and Wyoming
13. State bird of Maryland
17. State bird of Arkansas, Florida, and Mississippi
18. State bird of New York
19. State bird of Nevada
20. State bird of Colorado
23. State bird of Hawaii
25. State bird of Illinois and Ohio
27. State bird of Hawaii
31. State bird of South Carolina

Name ______________________ Date ______________

92. State Birds

93. STATE FLOWERS

ACROSS:

3. State flower of Nevada
4. State flower of Rhode Island
6. State flower of New York
11. State flower of Ohio
13. State flower of Alaska
14. State flower of Iowa
16. State flower of Hawaii
18. State flower of Arizona
21. State flower of North Dakota
22. State flower of Alaska
24. State flower of Utah
25. State flower of Idaho
27. State flower of Illinois
28. State flower of Georgia
33. State flower of South Carolina
34. State flower of Iowa
36. State flower of Idaho
38. State flower of Louisiana and Mississippi
39. State flower of Kentucky
40. State flower of Oklahoma
41. State flower of Minnesota
43. State flower of Massachusetts
46. State flower of Missouri
47. State flower of South Dakota
48. State flower of New Hampshire

DOWN:

1. State flower of New Mexico
2. State flower of Maryland
5. State flower of Delaware
6. State flower of Washington and West Virginia
7. State flower of Colorado
8. State flower of Tennessee
9. State flower of New York
10. State flower of Indiana
12. State flower of Texas
15. State flower of Alabama
17. State flower of California
19. State flower of Kansas
20. State flower of Florida
23. State flower of Oregon
26. State flower of Nebraska
29. State flower of Idaho
30. State flower of Virginia and North Carolina
31. State flower of Montana
32. State flower of Vermont
35. State flower of Tennessee
37. State flower of New York
41. State flower of Connecticut and Pennsylvania
42. State flower of Tennessee
44. State flower of New Mexico
45. State flower of Indiana

Name ______________________________ Date ______________________

93. State Flowers

94. STATE TREES

ACROSS:

1. Dogwood
4. Ponderosa pine
7. Paloverde
10. Palmetto
11. White pine
14. Hemlock
15. Sitka spruce
16. Red maple
20. Coffee tree
23. Live oak
24. Pecan
25. Pine
27. Blue spruce
30. Western white pine
31. Sabal palm
33. Sugar maple
34. Redbud
37. Bald cypress
39. Cottonwood
40. Sugar maple
42. White pine
43. Black Hills spruce

DOWN:

2. Douglas fir
3. Oak
5. Pecan
6. Southern pine
8. Single-leaf piñon
9. Magnolia
12. White oak
13. Western hemlock
17. White birch
18. Blue spruce
19. American elm
21. Blue spruce
22. American holly
26. Candlenut
28. White oak
29. White oak
30. Tulip poplar
32. Redwood
35. Candlenut
36. Oak
38. Oak
41. Oak

Name ______________________________ Date ____________________

94. State Trees

1 2 3 4 5 6 7 8 9 10 11 12 13 14 15 16 17 18 19 20 21 22 23 24 25 26 27 28 29 30 31 32 33 34 35 36 37 38 39 40 41 42 43

95. STATE SONGS

ACROSS:

1. "My Old ______ Home"
4. "Our ______"
7. "Carry Me Back to Old ______"
9. "______"
12. "The Song of ______"
13. "Home Means ______"
14. "The ______ Waltz"
17. "I Love ______"
18. "______, My ______"
19. "The Song of ______"
20. "______ Ponoi"
23. "The Song of ______"
26. "______"
27. "______ Ponoi"
28. "Beautiful ______"
29. "______"
30. "Beautiful ______"
32. "Beautiful ______"
34. "______ Hymn"
37. "The Song of ______"
38. "______'s Flag"
39. "I Love You, ______"
42. "______"
43. "Beautiful ______"
44. "______"
45. "______, Our ______"
48. "O Fair ______"
49. "On the Banks of the Wabash, Far Away"
50. "Old ______"

DOWN:

2. "______, We Love Thee"
3. "Here We Have ______"
5. "______, My Home Sweet Home"
6. "Yankee Doodle"
7. "Hail, ______"
8. "Home on the Range"
10. "On the Banks of the Wabash, Far Away"
11. "______ on My Mind"
15. "The Song of ______"
16. "______"
21. "On, ______"
22. "The Old North State"
24. "______: The March"
25. "Hail ______"
31. "Go ______"
33. "______"
35. "______"
36. "______, My ______"
39. "Where the Columbines Grow"
40. "Old Folks at Home"
41. "______ Waltz"
45. "______, Our ______"
46. "______, We Love Thee"
47. "State of ______ Song"

Name ______________________ Date ______________

95. State Songs

1 2 3 4 5 6 7 8 9 10 11 12 13 14 15 16 17 18 19 20 21 22 23 24 25 26 27 28 29 30 31 32 33 34 35 36 37 38 39 40 41 42 43 44 45 46 47 48 49 50

96. LARGEST CITIES IN THE UNITED STATES

ACROSS: ___

2. Boston
6. Nashville
7. Portland
8. Portland
9. Albuquerque
11. Anchorage
13. Minneapolis
17. Salt Lake City
19. Honolulu
21. Cheyenne
22. Milwaukee
26. Providence
27. Detroit
29. Philadelphia
33. Des Moines
35. Burlington
36. Phoenix
39. New Orleans
40. Salt Lake City
42. Des Moines
43. Cleveland
45. Los Angeles
46. Indianapolis
50. Wichita
52. Des Moines
53. Wichita
54. Denver
55. Chicago
56. Las Vegas
57. Wilmington

DOWN: ___

1. Sioux Falls
3. Little Rock
4. Burlington
5. Atlanta
6. Houston
10. Seattle
12. Birmingham
14. Boise
15. Milwaukee
16. Jackson
18. Honolulu
20. Billings
22. Huntington
23. Omaha
24. St. Louis
25. Hartford
28. Las Vegas
30. Columbia
31. Tampa
32. Portland
34. Oklahoma City
35. Norfolk
37. Chicago
38. Manchester
41. Louisville
44. Baltimore
47. Las Vegas
48. New York City
49. Portland
51. Anchorage
52. Des Moines

In the puzzle, fill in the name of the state where each of the above cities is located.

Name ______________________________ Date ____________________

96. Largest Cities in the United States

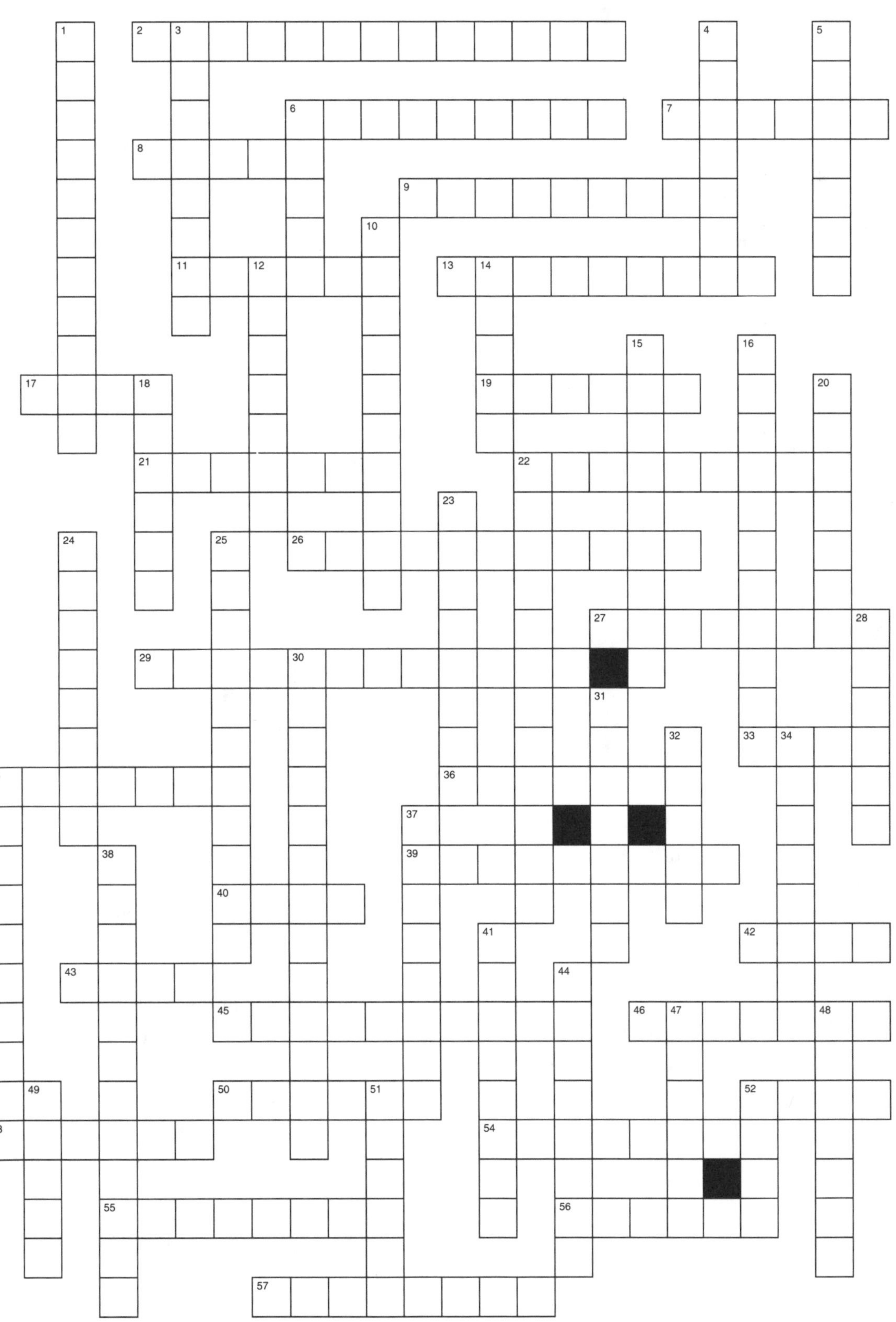

97. STATE INDUSTRIES

Identify the state by its leading industries and write its name in the blank provided. Then find the name of the state in the puzzle. Answers can be found horizontally, vertically, diagonally, and backward.

1. Pulp and paper, textiles, electronics, cotton
2. Computers, aerospace machinery, printing, publishing
3. Steel, clothing, coal mining, agriculture
4. Tobacco, textiles, furniture, tobacco products
5. Potatoes, lumber, silver mining, electronics
6. Oil and mineral production, insurance, real estate, cattle
7. Tobacco, coal mining, automotive assembly, lumber
8. Military aircraft, heavy machinery, lead mining, livestock
9. Potash mining, natural gas, tourism, cattle
10. Agriculture, lumber, boron mining, manufactured goods
11. Dairy products, eggs, lumber, tourism
12. Iron ore mining, hogs, beef cattle, food and paper products
13. Peanuts, peaches, poultry, marble mining
14. Corn, hogs, food processing, machinery manufacturing
15. Cattle, corn, wheat, gold mining
16. Hogs, limestone mining, auto parts, lumber products
17. Wood products, cattle, food processing, tourism
18. Copper mining, agriculture, electronics, lettuce
19. Aerospace, forestry products, apples, dairying
20. Wheat, beef cattle, helium, petroleum and gas
21. Dairy products, paper products, finance, cattle
22. Chemical manufacturing, chickens, soybeans, potatoes
23. Transportation equipment, coal mining, corn, soybeans
24. Apples, paper, fishing, lobstering
25. Furniture, maple syrup, apples, electronic equipment
26. Wheat, coal mining, farm machinery, railroad equipment
27. Printing and publishing, tourism, clothing, advertising
28. Motor vehicles, dairy products, iron mining, machinery
29. Petroleum and gas, cattle, wheat, fabricated metal products
30. Molybdenum mining, tourism, food processing, aerospace
31. Missile construction, electronics, sheep, copper mining
32. Livestock, farm machinery, shale mining, tires
33. Tourism, silver mining, processed foods, alfalfa
34. Citrus fruits, phosphate mining, tourism, fishing
35. Wheat, beef cattle, sunflower seeds, lignite mining
36. Oil and natural gas, salt mining, fishing, rice
37. Health services, jewelry, toys, ship building and boat building
38. Petroleum and gas, mining, wood pulp, gold
39. Wholesale and retail trade, chemical manufacturing, dairying, produce
40. Tourism, defense, pineapples, flowers
41. Cotton, transportation equipment, electrical equipment, clothing
42. Government services, tobacco, coal mining, textiles
43. Insurance, finance, real estate, submarines
44. Coal mining, stone, glass, timber
45. Finance, insurance, chemical manufacturing, dairying
46. Food processing, dairying, poultry, fishing
47. Tourism, cotton, textiles, chemical manufacturing
48. Chemicals, bauxite mining, petroleum and gas, rice
49. Oil and natural gas, uranium mining, cattle, sheep
50. Cattle, timber, wheat, mining

Name ______________________ Date ______________

97. State Industries

G W A M A B A L A O K L A H O M A D
N E E R A W A L E D O H I O W A R N
I N O H I S I L L I N O I S A A K A
M E E R O O S I D H W A H E N T A L
O V I W E I W A D A A O A I I O N S
Y A R N Y H H O C A I T T R L K S I
W D I U M O B O L H H C U D O A A E
U A K F I G R K O J U O I H R D S D
M T L E N M P K R O S S T N A H L O
U S A I N A V L Y S N N E P C T O H
T T L H E T E N I G E O X T H U U R
K A A X S E U M I O W A A E T O I T
A N S H O A S C A U M T S X R S S E
T E K S T D W I K T E A I A O W I N
O W A A A I O W A Y X R O S N A A N
K H A S E R H A W A I I A M Y S N E
A A I N R O F I L A C Z R O E H A S
D M S A O L A N A K O O N N S I T S
H P N K G F A S A S I N I T R N U E
T S A O I I N D I A N A S A E G C E
R H O N G E R O A R M W N N J T I D
O I B R I E I G I B H O O A W O T N
N R O O C H R I N E D I C S E N C A
V E R M O N T O I N U B S E N K E L
G O I H O S N A G I H C I M N A N Y
I T I E C O L O R A D O W A W S N R
O O I P P I S S I S S I M O I H 0 A
W E S T W E S T V I R G I N I A C M
A N I L O R A C H T U O S M A I N E

1. ______
2. ______
3. ______
4. ______
5. ______
6. ______
7. ______
8. ______
9. ______
10. ______
11. ______
12. ______
13. ______
14. ______
15. ______
16. ______
17. ______
18. ______
19. ______
20. ______
21. ______
22. ______
23. ______
24. ______
25. ______
26. ______
27. ______
28. ______
29. ______
30. ______
31. ______
32. ______
33. ______
34. ______
35. ______
36. ______
37. ______
38. ______
39. ______
40. ______
41. ______
42. ______
43. ______
44. ______
45. ______
46. ______
47. ______
48. ______
49. ______
50. ______

98. STATE SIZE

Identify the state by its size (in square miles) and write its name in the blank provided. Then find the name of the state in the puzzle. Answers can be found horizontally, vertically, diagonally, and backward.

1. 1,210
2. 2,045
3. 5,018
4. 6,471
5. 7,787
6. 8,284
7. 9,279
8. 9,609
9. 10,460
10. 24,231
11. 31,113
12. 33,265
13. 36,185
14. 40,409
15. 40,767
16. 41,330
17. 42,144
18. 45,308
19. 47,716
20. 47,752
21. 49,108
22. 51,705
23. 52,669
24. 53,187
25. 56,153
26. 56,275
27. 56,345
28. 58,527
29. 58,664
30. 58,876
31. 68,139
32. 69,697
33. 69,919
34. 70,702
35. 77,116
36. 77,227
37. 81,781
38. 83,564
39. 84,402
40. 84,899
41. 97,073
42. 97,809
43. 104,091
44. 110,561
45. 114,000
46. 121,593
47. 147,046
48. 158,706
49. 266,807
50. 591,004

Name ______________________________ Date ____________________

98. State Size

R C E G W I A N I L O R A C H T R O N S B E R G E
A A T E N N E S S E E E O H A D I S I T O U A N S
C F L I D N A L S I E D O H R I L O N T N O P I O
S T N A G I H C I M V A A E A I O U U E E D G M U
H J E K B L N D O R S T X W A U M T O S W E T O T
O I B B E A G E O R G I A G I K A H C U J Y N Y H
L O R P I R M L T A F H A L A B R C I H E C O W D
A D A V E N E A I K E N T U C K Y A X C R O M R A
A L S O U T K W I S C O U S A H L R E A S I R E K
N O K S A S N A K A N S C O L O A O M S E N E R O
E T A L A B A R H S O U I O W A N L W S Y O V I T
W A S L I N G E A S A R T E X S D I E A Z R W O A
H A A R I Z O N A L A X C A A L I N N M U T I A T
A D I R O L F L O O H I E S O U T A M I N H S E O
M S Y R I O W A I O W E N T E N I O H S E D C A B
P E I N N Z I H A W A A N O R S T K E S I A O I R
S R C O I H O H I O K A O H I O W A T I S K N N E
H A R R N O R N E R A S C U K A N M E S T O S I R
I O W A D I M C A L I F O R N I A N I S M T I G O
R I S S I S L O H I O L O U I I O W A I R A N R S
E A R O A T E L N O N E B R N E W Y S P E N N I S
I O W A N H I O I T E O F E R S T S O P I U T V I
B A U T A H A R R I A B G I R W O H I I O W A T U
N O R T H D A A C A L N I E S U G E O R G I A S T
S O U T H C A D I D A H A I R V I R G I N I A E O
E M I N N E S O T A I J O I N O T G N I H S A W Z
O R E G A I N A V L Y S N N E P O K L A H O M A E

1. ____________
2. ____________
3. ____________
4. ____________
5. ____________
6. ____________
7. ____________
8. ____________
9. ____________
10. ____________
11. ____________
12. ____________
13. ____________
14. ____________
15. ____________
16. ____________
17. ____________
18. ____________
19. ____________
20. ____________
21. ____________
22. ____________
23. ____________
24. ____________
25. ____________
26. ____________
27. ____________
28. ____________
29. ____________
30. ____________
31. ____________
32. ____________
33. ____________
34. ____________
35. ____________
36. ____________
37. ____________
38. ____________
39. ____________
40. ____________
41. ____________
42. ____________
43. ____________
44. ____________
45. ____________
46. ____________
47. ____________
48. ____________
49. ____________
50. ____________

99. STATE POPULATION DENSITY
(PER SQUARE MILE AS OF 1990)

ACROSS:

4. 183
5. 33
8. 33
10. 210
11. 30
12. 81
14. 261
15. 110
18. 37
19. 172
21. 124
23. 53
28. 11
29. 1
30. 63
31. 172
32. 978
36. 88
37. 20
38. 91
39. 88
40. 116
42. 9
44. 63
45. 150
46. 49
48. 817
49. 201

DOWN:

1. 210
2. 452
3. 49
4. 33
6. 73
7. 71
9. 74
13. 5
16. 119
17. 51
18. 157
20. 12
22. 46
24. 12
25. 49
26. 260
27. 716
33. 87
34. 81
35. 49
41. 29
43. 172
47. 261

Name ____________________ Date ____________________

99. State Population Density

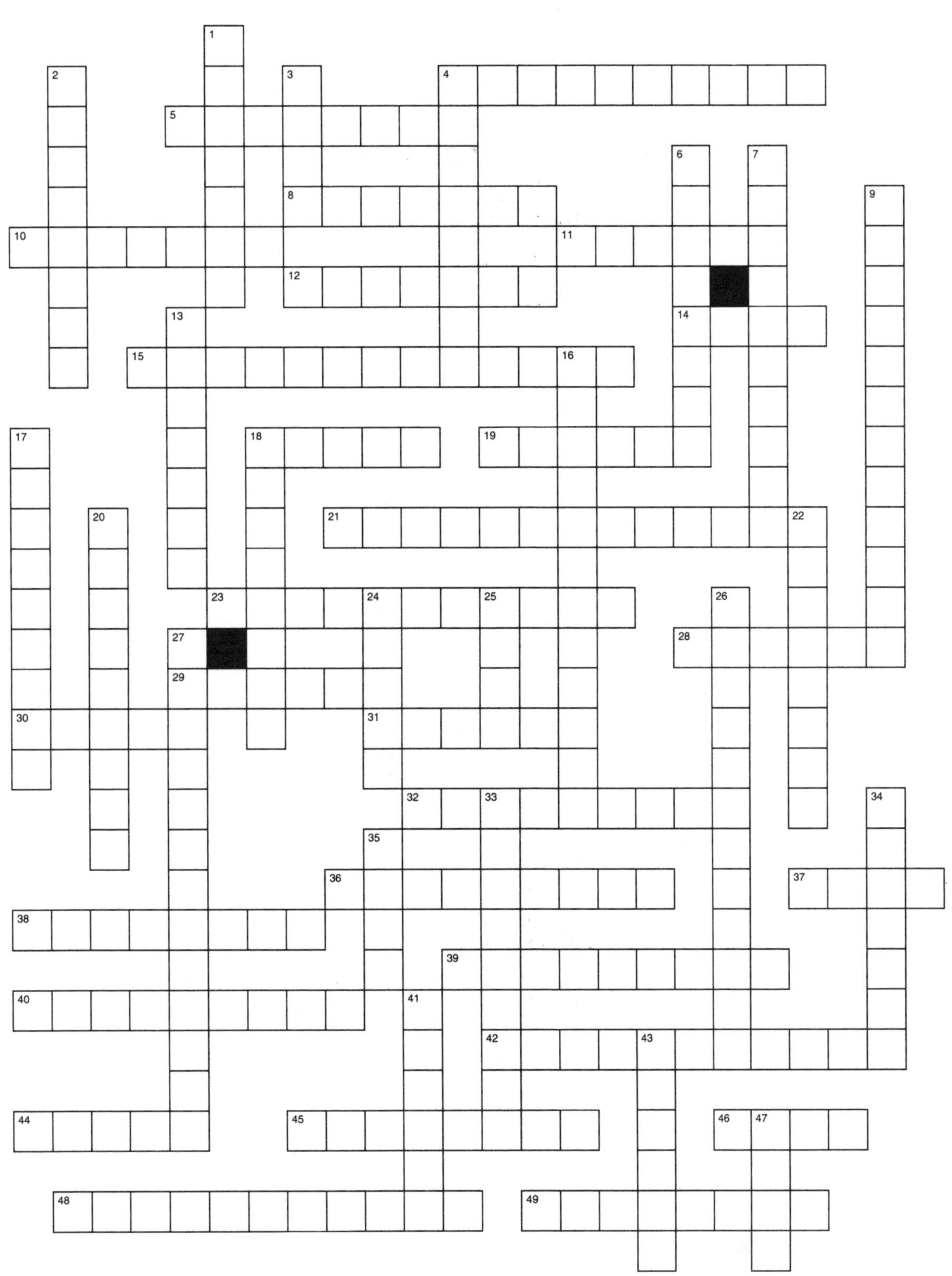

100. STATE DATE OF ENTRY INTO THE UNION

ACROSS: ____________________

1. 1959
4. 1907
9. 1818
11. 1959
12. 1821
13. 1787
16. 1845
19. 1889
21. 1787
22. 1890
24. 1837
28. 1812
30. 1850
32. 1896
33. 1846
34. 1959
36. 1790
39. 1836
42. 1896
44. 1816
45. 1889
46. 1803
47. 1876
48. 1788
49. 1845

DOWN: ____________________

2. 1846
3. 1788
5. 1820
6. 1912
7. 1817
8. 1845
10. 1803
14. 1863
15. 1859
17. 1845
18. 1796
20. 1890
23. 1876
25. 1858
26. 1787
27. 1792
29. 1788
31. 1861
35. 1846
37. 1890
38. 1848
39. 1912
40. 1861
41. 1819
43. 1896

Name ______________________ Date ______________

100. State Date of Entry into the Union

101. STATE ORDER OF ENTRY INTO THE UNION

ACROSS:

3. Thirty-eighth state
4. Forty-second state
7. Fortieth state
9. Sixth state
12. Twenty-eighth state
13. Nineteenth state
18. Ninth state
20. Forty-fifth state
21. Twentieth state
22. Seventeenth state
23. First state
25. Forty-fifth state
27. Twenty-fifth state
29. Forty-fifth state
31. Fiftieth state
33. Forty-eighth state
34. Twenty-ninth state
36. Thirty-seventh state
37. Thirty-first state
39. Twenty-third state
41. Thirty-sixth state
43. Eighth state
45. Thirty-third state
46. Eleventh state
47. Fourteenth state
50. Thirty-ninth state
52. Thirty-fourth state
53. Twenty-ninth state
54. Twenty-third state
55. Sixteenth state
56. Forty-fourth state

DOWN:

1. Twenty-ninth state
2. Forty-first state
3. Fifth state
5. Twenty-ninth state
6. Forty-third state
8. Eighteenth state
10. Twenty-eighth state
11. Forty-seventh state
14. Twenty-first state
15. Second state
16. Tenth state
17. Thirty-fifth state
19. Forty-ninth state
22. Forth-sixth state
24. Thirteenth state
26. Twenty-fourth state
28. Third state
30. Fourth state
32. Twelfth state
35. Seventh state
38. Twenty-second state
39. Twenty-third state
40. Forty-third state
42. Twenty-seventh state
44. Seventeenth state
48. Twenty-third state
49. Twenty-ninth state
51. Seventeenth state

Name ______________________ Date ______________________

101. State Order of Entry into the Union

102. FAMOUS SONS AND DAUGHTERS—I

Identify the state by its famous people.

ACROSS: ____________________

1. Joe DiMaggio and William Randolph Hearst
2. Hank Williams and W. C. Handy
3. Robert Frost and Franklin Pierce
4. Jack Dempsey and Douglas Fairbanks
5. Leonard Bernstein and Emily Dickinson
6. Amelia Earhart and Carry Nation
7. Louis Armstrong and Truman Capote
8. Jackie Robinson and Juliette Gordon Low
9. Ernest Hemingway and Ronald Reagan
10. Jefferson Davis and Elvis Presley
11. Ezra Pound and John Gutzon Borglum
12. Warren E. Burger and Sinclair Lewis
13. Crazy Horse and Sitting Bull
14. Mary McLeod Bethune and Joseph Stilwell
15. Douglas MacArthur and Dizzy Dean
16. Mohammed Ali and Zachary Taylor
17. Henry Ford and Sojourner Truth
18. Nathaniel Hawthorne and John F. Kennedy
19. Noah Webster and Eli Whitney
20. Bob Dylan and F. Scott Fitzgerald
21. Jimmy Carter and Ty Cobb
22. Jean Lafitte and Huey Long

Name ______________________________ Date ____________________

102. Famous Sons and Daughters—I

Clue	Printed letter
1	F
2	A
3	M
4	O
5	U
6	S
7	S
8	O
9	N
10	S
11	A
12	N
13	D
14	D
15	A
16	U
17	G
18	H
19	T
20	E
21	R
22	S

103. FAMOUS SONS AND DAUGHTERS—II

Identify the state by its famous people.

ACROSS: ______________________________

1. George S. Patton and John Steinbeck
2. Frederick Douglass and Johns Hopkins
3. Helen Keller and Willie Mays
4. Buffalo Bill Cody and Herbert Hoover
5. Cassius Marcellus Clay and Abraham Lincoln
6. Eddy Arnold and Davy Crockett
7. Andrew Jackson and Alvin York
8. Barry Goldwater and Sandra Day O'Connor
9. Henry Wadsworth Longfellow and Edmund Muskie
10. Tennessee Williams and Richard Wright
11. John Dickinson and Eleuthere Irenee du Pont
12. Judy Garland and Charles Lindbergh
13. James Dean and Eugene V. Debs
14. Anne Hutchinson and Matthew C. Perry
15. Johnny Carson and Fred Astaire
16. Josephine Baker and Jesse James
17. Richard E. Byrd and Patrick Henry
18. Bing Crosby and James Whittaker
19. Gary Cooper and Jeannette Rankin
20. J. P. Morgan and Harriet Beecher Stowe
21. Margaret Mitchell and Martin Luther King, Jr.
22. Joseph Pulitzer and Harry S Truman

Name ______________________________ Date ____________________

103. Famous Sons and Daughters—II

1				F					
2				A					
3				M					
4				O					
5				U					
6				S					
7				S					
8				O					
9				N					
10				S					
11				A					
12				N					
13				D					
14				D					
15				A					
16				U					
17				G					
18				H					
19				T					
20				E					
21				R					
22				S					

104. FAMOUS SONS AND DAUGHTERS—III

Identify the state by its famous people.

ACROSS: ____

1. Osceola and Marjorie Kinnan Rawlings
2. Thomas Wolfe and James B. Duke
3. Ethan Allen and Chester A. Arthur
4. Neil Armstrong and Clarence Darrow
5. W.E.B. DuBois and Norman Rockwell
6. Marian Anderson and Andrew Carnegie
7. Sam Houston and Howard Hughes
8. John L. Lewis and Lillian Russell
9. Jane Addams and Jack Benny
10. Harry Houdini and Spencer Tracy
11. Althea Gibson and John C. Calhoun
12. Robert E. Perry and Edna St. Vincent Millay
13. George M. Cohan and Nathanael Greene
14. Gus Grissom and Madame C. J. Walker
15. Joe Louis and Jesse Owens
16. George Washington Carver and John J. Pershing
17. Pearl S. Buck and Chuck Yeager
18. Louis L'Amour and Peggy Lee
19. P. T. Barnum and Samuel Colt
20. Billy the Kid and Conrad Hilton
21. Thurgood Marshall and Babe Ruth
22. Medgar Evers and William Faulkner

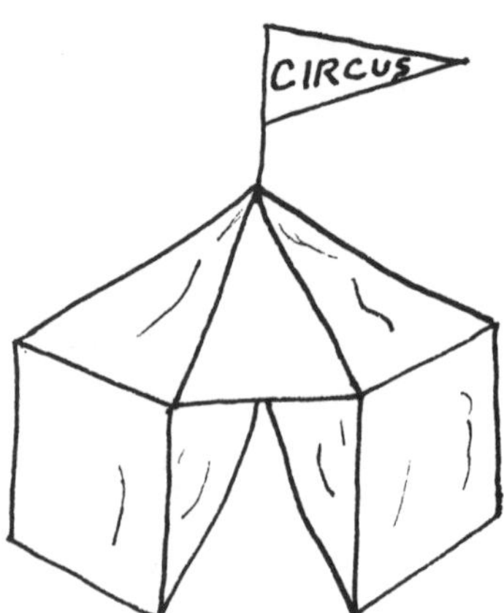

Name ______________________ Date ______________

104. Famous Sons and Daughters—III

1 F
2 A
3 M
4 O
5 U
6 S

7 S
8 O
9 N
10 S

11 A
12 N
13 D

14 D
15 A
16 U
17 G
18 H
19 T
20 E
21 R
22 S

105. FAMOUS SONS AND DAUGHTERS—IV

Identify the state by its famous people.

ACROSS: ______

1. Isadora Duncan and Richard Nixon
2. Oliver Wendell Holmes, Jr., and Henry David Thoreau
3. Kit Carson and Georgia O'Keeffe
4. George Gershwin and Franklin D. Roosevelt
5. Jesse James and George Washington Carver
6. Andrew Johnson and James K. Polk
7. Hubert H. Humphrey and William O. Douglas
8. Edward V. Rickenbacker and Orville Wright
9. Cole Porter and Knute Rockne
10. George W. Norris and Darryl F. Zanuck
11. Harriet Tubman and Upton Sinclair
12. Carl Sandburg and Adlai Stevenson
13. Eric Sevareid and Lawrence Welk
14. Oliver H. Perry and Roger Williams
15. Maude Adams and Brigham Young
16. Zachary Taylor and Abraham Lincoln
17. Martin R. Delany and "Stonewall" Jackson
18. Woodie Guthrie and Mickey Mantle
19. Edward R. Murrow and O. Henry
20. Aaron Burr and Stephen Crane
21. Billy Graham and Dolley Madison
22. Stephen Foster and Benjamin Franklin

Name ______________________________ Date ____________________

105. Famous Sons and Daughters—IV

1 F
2 A
3 M
4 O
5 U
6 S

7 S
8 O
9 N
10 S

11 A
12 N
13 D

14 D
15 A
16 U
17 G
18 H
19 T
20 E
21 R
22 S

106. FAMOUS SONS AND DAUGHTERS—V

Identify the state by its famous people.

ACROSS: ______________________________

1. Joseph W. Stilwell and Mary McLeod Bethune
2. Edgar Allan Poe and Walter Reed
3. Jim Bridger and Nellie Tayloe Ross
4. Jonas Salk and Theodore Roosevelt
5. Edward Douglass White and Louis Armstrong
6. Thomas Edison and Woodrow Wilson
7. Daniel Webster and Alan B. Shepard
8. John Glenn and Annie Oakley
9. Charles Goodyear and Nathan Hale
10. Robert Fulton and George Marshall
11. Will Rogers and Jim Thorpe
12. William Jennings Bryan and Walt Disney
13. Eugene V. Debs and Cole Porter
14. George McGovern and Hallie Flanagan
15. Mary Martin and Babe Didrickson Zaharias
16. John Moses Browning and George Romney
17. Cyrus McCormick and Robert E. Lee
18. James Thurber and William Tecumseh Sherman
19. Charles Lindbergh and F. Scott Fitzgerald
20. George Eastman and Grover Cleveland
21. George Dewey and Calvin Coolidge
22. Marlon Brando and Dick Cavett

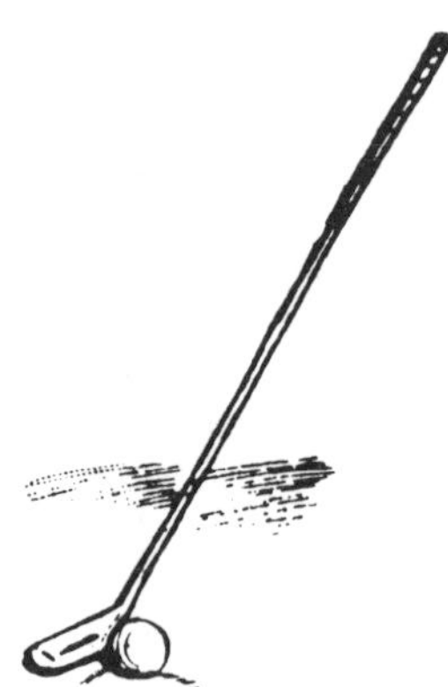

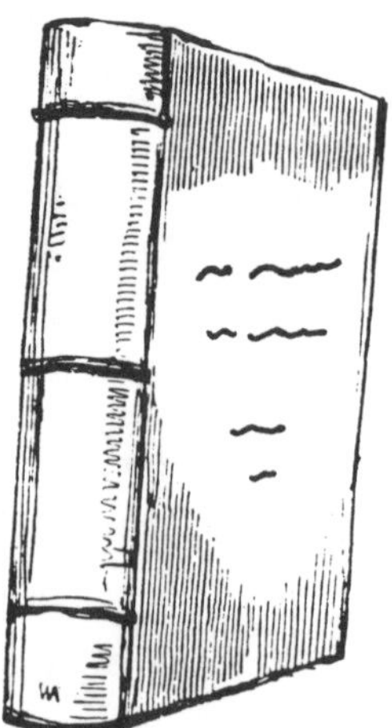

Name ______________________ Date ______________

106. Famous Sons and Daughters—V

1 F
2 A
3 M
4 O
5 U
6 S

7 S
8 O
9 N
10 S

11 A
12 N
13 D

14 D
15 A
16 U
17 G
18 H
19 T
20 E
21 R
22 S

107. FAMOUS SONS AND DAUGHTERS—VI

Identify the state by its famous people.

ACROSS: ______________________________

1. Jack London and Isadora Duncan
2. J. William Fulbright and Edward Durell Stone
3. Mary Baker Eddy and Daniel Chester French
4. Meredith Willson and Henry A. Wallace
5. Robert Penn Warren and Jesse Stuart
6. Susan Butcher and Ernest Gruening
7. Charles Curtis and Charlie Parker
8. Clark Gable and Harvey Firestone
9. Winslow Homer and Andrew Wyeth
10. Eudora Welty and Leontyne Price
11. Thomas Francis Bayard and Annie Jump Cannon
12. Carl T. Hayden and Percival Lowell
13. William Edgar Borah and Vardis Fisher
14. Marjorie Kinnan Rawlings and Joseph W. Stilwell
15. William Morris Stewart and Wovoka
16. Dale Carnegie and Virgil Thomson
17. Sidney Lanier and Carson McCullers
18. Ralph Bunche and Edna Ferber
19. Mike Mansfield and A. B. Guthrie, Jr.
20. John Reed and Linus Pauling
21. Byron R. White and Paul Whiteman
22. Howard Rock and Don Sheldon

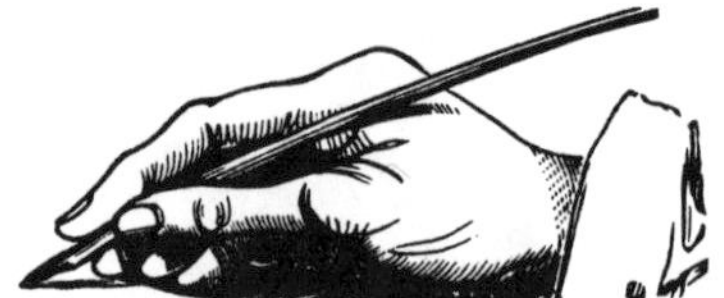

Name ________________________________ Date ____________________

107. Famous Sons and Daughters—VI

F
A
M
O
U
S

S
O
N
S

A
N
D

D
A
U
G
H
T
E
R
S

1 2 3 4 5 6 7 8 9 10 11 12 13 14 15 16 17 18 19 20 21 22

108. STATE HISTORICAL HIGHLIGHTS—I

Identify the state by its historical highlight.

ACROSS: ____

1. Dartmouth College opened in Hanover in 1769
2. Custer's Last Stand at the Battle of the Little Bighorn in 1876
3. The United States was attacked by the Japanese in 1941
4. The U.S. Coast Guard Academy moved to New London in 1910
5. Americans were defeated at the Alamo in 1836
6. Oberlin, the nation's first coeducational college, opened in 1833
7. World's Columbian Exposition was held in 1893
8. Union troops captured Vicksburg, a turning point in the Civil War, in 1863
9. Brigham Young brought Mormon pioneers here in 1847
10. George Washington was inaugurated as the first U.S. president in 1789
11. First state to give eighteen-year-olds the vote in 1943
12. The Revolutionary War ended at Yorktown in 1781
13. The first Derby horse race was held in 1875
14. Rev. Martin Luther King, Jr., led a march from Selma to Montgomery in 1965
15. The battle of Fort Sumter began the Civil War in 1861
16. The nation's first subway system opened here in 1897
17. Race riots occurred in Watts in 1965
18. Richmond became the Confederate capital in 1861
19. Mt. St. Helens erupted here in 1980
20. The U.S. Naval Academy was founded here in 1845
21. Gold was discovered in Gila City in 1858
22. John Brown was captured at Harpers Ferry in 1859
23. American Indian Movement members occupied the village of Wounded Knee for seventy-one days in 1973
24. The Green Mountain Boys captured Fort Ticonderoga in 1775
25. Casino gambling started in Atlantic City in 1978

Name ____________________ Date ____________________

108. State Historical Highlights—I

1 S
2 T
3 A
4 T
5 E

6 H
7 I
8 S
9 T
10 O
11 R
12 I
13 C
14 A
15 L

16 H
17 I
18 G
19 H
20 L
21 I
22 G
23 H
24 T
25 S

109. STATE HISTORICAL HIGHLIGHTS—II

Identify the state by its historical highlight.

ACROSS: ____

1. The Dred Scott case was tried here in 1857
2. The nation's first ski tow was built in Woodstock in 1934
3. Union troops won the battle of Antietam in 1862
4. The gold depository at Fort Knox was installed in 1936
5. The first atomic bomb was tested near Alamogordo in 1945
6. The first baseball World Series was played here in 1903
7. The battle of Tippecanoe was fought in 1811
8. The first state lottery in the United States was held here in 1964
9. Yale College was founded here in 1701
10. The first intercontinental ballistic missile base was established at Cheyenne in 1960
11. The Erie Canal opened here in 1825
12. Riots occurred at the Democratic National Convention in 1968
13. Hurricane Hugo devastated this coastal area in 1989
14. Tuskegee Institute opened here in 1881
15. The first rocket was launched at Cape Canaveral in 1950
16. In the first U.S. execution in ten years, Gary Gilmore was killed by a firing squad at Provo in 1977
17. Geronimo surrendered here in 1886
18. The Civil War ended at Appomattox in 1865
19. Gold was discovered in the Black Hills in 1874
20. The U.S. Air Force Academy moved to its present home in 1958
21. The first Mardi Gras was held here in 1838
22. Eli Whitney invented the cotton gin here in 1793
23. U.S. troops defeated Native Americans at the battle of Fallen Timbers in 1794
24. President John F. Kennedy was assassinated here in 1963
25. James Meredith became the first African American to enter a major southern college here in 1962

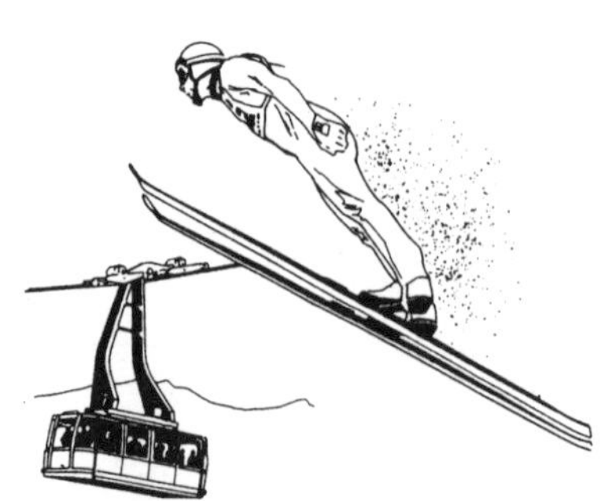

Name ______________________ Date ______________________

109. State Historical Highlights—II

1 __ __ S __ __ __ __ __

2 __ __ __ __ __ __ T

3 __ A __ __ __ __ __ __

4 __ __ __ T __ __ __ __

5 __ __ __ __ E __ __ __ __

6 __ __ __ __ __ __ H __ __ __ __ __ __

7 __ __ __ I __ __ __

8 __ __ __ __ __ __ __ S __ __ __ __

9 __ __ __ __ __ __ T __ __ __ __

10 __ __ O __ __ __ __

11 __ __ __ __ __ R __

12 __ __ __ I __ __ __ __

13 __ __ __ __ __ C __ __ __ __ __ __ __

14 __ __ __ __ A __ __

15 __ L __ __ __ __ __ __

16 __ __ __ H

17 __ __ I __ __ __ __ __

18 __ __ __ G __ __ __ __

19 __ __ __ __ H __ __ __ __ __ __

20 __ __ L __ __ __ __ __ __

21 __ __ __ I __ __ __ __ __ __

22 G __ __ __ __ __ __ __

23 __ H __ __

24 T __ __ __ __

25 __ __ __ __ __ S __ __ __ __ __

110. STATE HISTORICAL HIGHLIGHTS—III

Identify the state by its historical highlight.

ACROSS: ______________________________

1. The first Indian reservation in America was established here in 1758
2. Chief Joseph and the Nez Percé Indians surrendered here in 1877
3. Integration of Central High School in Little Rock in 1957
4. Daniel Boone first crossed the Cumberland Gap in 1767
5. The Statue of Liberty was dedicated here in 1886
6. Federal troops killed two hundred Sioux at Wounded Knee Creek in 1890
7. A Cincinnati art museum was acquitted of obscenity charges for exhibiting the photographs of Robert Maplethorpe in 1990
8. Martin Luther King, Jr., was assassinated here in 1968
9. First telephone exchange in the world started at New Haven in 1878
10. The gunfight at the O.K. Corral occurred in 1881
11. Gold was discovered at Cherry Creek in 1859
12. Gold was discovered at Sutter's Mill in 1848
13. Twenty people were executed in Salem for witchcraft in 1692
14. Andrew Jackson defeated the Creek Indians at Horseshoe Bend in 1814
15. Walt Disney World opened here in 1971
16. Settlers defeated the Native Americans here in King Philip's War in 1676
17. The first Indianapolis 500 auto race was run here in 1911
18. The first African American governor in U.S. history was elected here in 1989
19. Four Kent State University students were killed here by National Guardsmen during a campus protest over the Vietnam War in 1970
20. The U.S. Mint in Denver opened in 1906
21. Andrew Jackson won the battle of New Orleans in 1815
22. Cherokee Indians began the "Trail of Tears" in 1838
23. Gold was discovered on the Clearwater River in 1860
24. The Wilderness Road and Fort Boonesborough were built here in 1775
25. Oil was discovered near Jennings in 1901

Name ______________________________ Date ____________________

110. State Historical Highlights—III

1 S
2 T
3 A
4 T
5 E

6 H
7 I
8 S
9 T
10 O
11 R
12 I
13 C
14 A
15 L

16 H
17 I
18 G
19 H
20 L
21 I
22 G
23 H
24 T
25 S

111. STATE HISTORICAL HIGHLIGHTS-IV

Identify the state by its historical highlight.

ACROSS:

1. Fort Leavenworth was built on the Santa Fe Trail in 1827
2. America's first law school opened at Litchfield in 1784
3. The Revolutionary War began here in 1775
4. The atomic research plant at Oak Ridge was built in 1942
5. Samuel Morse invented the telegraph at Morristown in 1838
6. William Lloyd Garrison published the *Liberator* in 1831
7. Huey Long was assassinated here in 1935
8. The most severe earthquake in North American history occurred here in 1964
9. A coal mine explosion near Wooten killed 38 people in 1970
10. The stock market crashed in 1929
11. Crazy Horse surrendered at Fort Robinson in 1877
12. The space shuttle *Challenger* exploded in 1986
13. The first atomic-powered submarine, the *Nautilus,* was built here in 1954
14. Silver was discovered in the Wood River area in 1880
15. The Toleration Act was passed here in 1649
16. The first professional baseball team was founded here in 1869
17. An earthquake devastated San Francisco in 1906
18. The first African American mayor of a major southern city, Maynard Jackson, Jr., was elected here in 1973
19. The Pilgrims on the *Mayflower* landed here in 1620
20. The nation's first civil rights monument was dedicated here in 1989
21. The Great Chicago Fire occurred here in 1871
22. General Sherman's "March to the Sea" occurred here in 1864
23. The first U.S. nuclear power plant was built at Arco in 1946
24. Noah Webster published the first American dictionary here in 1806
25. The first oil well in America was drilled at Titusville in 1859

Name ______________________________ Date ____________________

111. State Historical Highlights—IV

1 S
2 T
3 A
4 T
5 E

6 H
7 I
8 S
9 T
10 O
11 R
12 I
13 C
14 A
15 L

16 H
17 I
18 G
19 H
20 L
21 I
22 G
23 H
24 T
25 S

112. STATE HISTORICAL HIGHLIGHTS—V

Identify the state by its historical highlight.

ACROSS: ______

1. Gold was discovered in Nome in 1899
2. A hurricane in Galveston killed six thousand people in 1900
3. Admiral David Farragut shouted, "Damn the torpedoes, full steam ahead," at Mobile Bay in 1864
4. The first transcontinental railroad was completed at Promontory in 1869
5. Americans won their first battle of the Revolutionary War at Trenton in 1776
6. Nicola Sacco and Bartolomeo Vanzetti were executed here for murder in 1927
7. The first film was made in Hollywood in 1910
8. The Declaration of Independence was signed here in 1776
9. The U.S. gold depository at Fort Knox was established here in 1936
10. President William McKinley was assassinated here in 1901
11. Site of the United Nations beginning in 1946
12. The Haymarket Riot killed eight people here in 1886
13. The nation's first unemployment compensation law was passed here in 1932
14. Gambling was legalized here in 1869
15. Rosa Parks was arrested here for refusing to give up her seat on a Montgomery bus in 1955
16. Gutzon Borglum began carving Mt. Rushmore here in 1927
17. The Golden Gate Bridge opened here in 1937
18. Grand Coulee Dam opened here in 1942
19. Standard Oil Company was organized here by John D. Rockefeller in 1870
20. The nation's first railroad, the Baltimore and Ohio, began here in 1828
21. The College of William and Mary admitted women in 1918
22. The Carter Presidential Center opened here in 1986
23. Dartmouth College opened here in 1769
24. The "Monkey Trial" on teaching evolution in schools was held here in 1925
25. The case of *Brown v. Board of Education* was filed here in 1951

Name ______________________________ Date ____________________

112. State Historical Highlights—V

1 S
2 T
3 A
4 T
5 E

6 H
7 I
8 S
9 T
10 O
11 R
12 I
13 C
14 A
15 L

16 H
17 I
18 G
19 H
20 L
21 I
22 G
23 H
24 T
25 S

113. STATE HISTORICAL HIGHLIGHTS—VI

Identify the state by its historical highlight.

ACROSS: ____

1. Three young civil rights workers were killed near the town of Philadelphia in 1964
2. The first state to secede from the Union in 1860
3. The largest oil spill in U.S. history occurred here in 1989
4. Congress established Glacier National Park in 1910
5. The source of the Mississippi River was discovered at Lake Itasca in 1832
6. The Soo Ship Canal and Locks, linking Lakes Huron and Superior, opened in 1855
7. One million acres of Yellowstone National Park burned in 1988
8. Pony Express service started in St. Joseph in 1860
9. The first English colony in America was built on Roanoke Island in 1585
10. Grand Canyon National Park was established here in 1919
11. Everglades National Park was established here in 1947
12. Margaret Chase Smith became the first woman to serve in both houses of Congress in 1948
13. The Republican party was founded in the town of Ripon in 1854
14. The Strategic Air Command, the U.S. Air Force's long-range attack group, was established here in 1946
15. Site of the Lincoln–Douglas debates in 1858
16. Basketball was invented here by Dr. James Naismith in 1891
17. The Gateway Arch, the nation's tallest monument, was completed in 1965
18. The first permanent English settlement in America was founded in 1607
19. In Greensboro, African American students remained seated at a restricted lunch counter after they were refused service in 1960, leading to a series of sit-in demonstrations throughout the state
20. State that donated the land for the District of Columbia in 1791
21. Nat Turner's rebellion in 1831 led to stricter slavery laws
22. Crater Lake National Park was established in 1902
23. Detroit's first automobile plant was built in 1900
24. Theodore Roosevelt National Park was established in 1947
25. Accident at Three Mile Island nuclear power plant near Harrisburg threatened the release of radiation in 1979

Name ______________________________ Date ____________________

113. State Historical Highlights—VI

1 S
2 T
3 A
4 T
5 E

6 H
7 I
8 S
9 T
10 O
11 R
12 I
13 C
14 A
15 L

16 H
17 I
18 G
19 H
20 L
21 I
22 G
23 H
24 T
25 S

114. STATE ODDITIES AND SPECIALTIES—I

Identify the state by its oddity or specialty.

ACROSS: ____________________

1. The first Arbor Day was celebrated here in 1872
2. Nation's leading producer of tobacco, textiles, and furniture
3. The oldest continuously published newspaper west of the Mississippi River was founded here in 1819
4. Host of the oldest continuously run horse race in America
5. Has well over ten thousand lakes
6. Has the world's largest and deepest spring, Wakulla Springs
7. Resting place for the legendary Johnny Appleseed, John Chapman
8. Has more allocated wilderness than any state except Alaska
9. Only state in the Union that borders just one other state
10. First in the world for the production of bourbon
11. Location of the world's most devastating tornado in 1925
12. Its citizens have filed more patents per capita than any other state
13. Geographic center of the contiguous states
14. Heaviest meteor shower ever recorded occurred here in 1833
15. Produced the first self-sustaining nuclear reaction in 1942
16. The nation's gambling capital
17. 80 percent of the terrain is permanently frozen in this state
18. Its state legislature is the largest in the nation
19. Nation's marriage capital
20. Implemented the first U.S. auto speed limit, twelve miles per hour
21. First in the nation for salt production
22. Produces at least seventy kinds of precious and semiprecious stones
23. Location of America's first umbrella factory in 1828
24. Location of the Hatfield–McCoy feud
25. Has the most motor vehicles per square mile in the world
26. Held the first organized baseball game in 1846
27. The first heart and lung transplant took place here in 1963

Name ______________________ Date ______________

114. State Oddities and Specialties—I

115. STATE ODDITIES AND SPECIALTIES—II

Identify the state by its oddity or specialty.

ACROSS:

1. The leading producer of helium in the United States
2. Mother's Day was conceived in the town of Henderson by schoolteacher Mary Wilson in 1887
3. Has the oldest U.S. Protestant church to still hold regular services
4. The football tackling dummy and T-formation were invented by Amos Alonzo Stagg at Yale in 1889
5. Home of the mythical hero Paul Bunyan and his blue ox, Babe
6. Where John Brown trained his men for the attack on Harpers Ferry
7. Taxes from gambling provide 40 percent of this state's revenues
8. Boasts America's oldest carousel, the Flying Horse
9. Birthplace of jazz
10. The first American commercial jet was made here
11. The London Bridge was moved here in 1962
12. Its city of Macon boasts more cherry trees than any other U.S. city
13. Only state with a unicameral, or one-house, legislature
14. Produces the only commercial coffee beans in the United States
15. Produces parking meters used worldwide
16. Produced the largest diamond in the nation, 10.5 carats
17. Hosted the first Little League baseball game and symphony orchestra performance
18. Nation's catfish capital
19. Hosted the first intercollegiate football game in 1869
20. Has 106 colleges
21. Location of the first metal-framed skyscraper, the Home Insurance Building
22. Produces one of every eight broiler chickens eaten in the United States
23. Its Preakness Stakes, an annual horse race, is part of the Triple Crown
24. World speed records have been set at the Bonneville Salt Flats
25. Location of the southernmost point in the United States
26. Produces nearly half of the nation's uranium
27. Leads the nation in the production of upholstered furniture

Name ______________________________ Date ____________________

115. State Oddities and Specialties—II

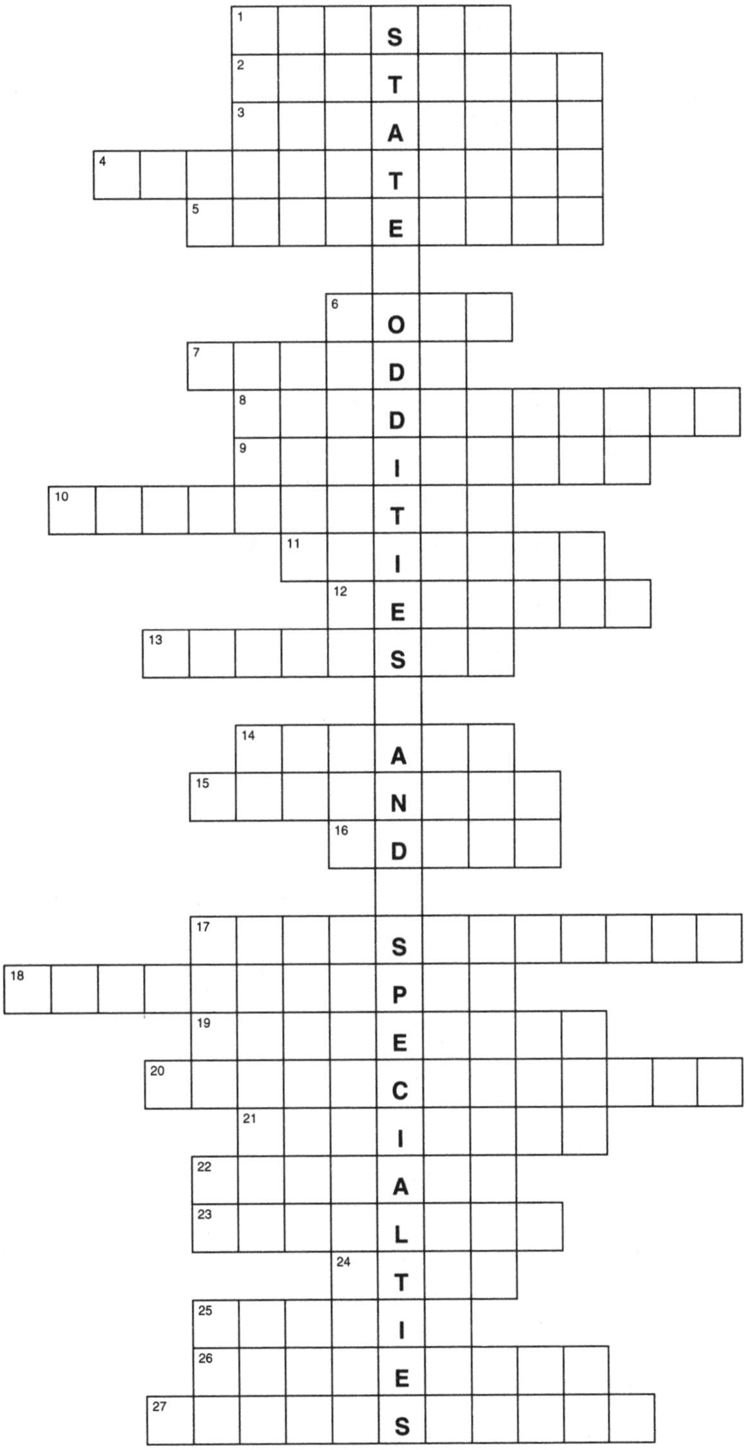

116. STATE ODDITIES AND SPECIALTIES—III

Identify the state by its oddity or specialty.

ACROSS: ____

1. Location of seventeen of the twenty highest peaks in the United States
2. Host of the National Hollering Contest each year
3. Where Dr. John H. Kellogg of Battle Creek created Cornflakes
4. Host of the country's largest state fair
5. Location of the oldest capital city in the United States
6. Published the first newspaper in a Native American language, Cherokee
7. Its average elevation, 6,800 feet, is the highest of any state
8. Hosts the nation's oldest Independence Day parade
9. Location of the world's tallest building, the Sears Tower (1,454 feet)
10. Has the smallest capital city in the nation
11. Location of the world's oldest living organisms, bristlecone pine trees
12. The Miss America pageant is held here annually
13. Boasts the "World's Largest Fish Fry," over eighty-five hundred pounds of catfish
14. 90 percent of its plants and wildlife are found no place else in the world
15. The leading producer of apples in the United States
16. Has the country's oldest Jewish house of worship
17. Produces more corncob pipes than anywhere else in the world
18. Its university holds the world's largest collection of blues music
19. Location of the first dinosaur skeleton discovered in North America
20. Boasts the oldest college in America, Harvard
21. State added to the Union by the Missouri Compromise
22. First state to ratify the Constitution
23. Produced the largest silver nugget ever discovered in North America, 1,840 pounds
24. Country's largest marble production center
25. The first electronic digital computer was built at this state university in 1939
26. The *Hindenburg* crashed here in 1937
27. Has the highest average wind speed in the United States, 13.4 miles per hour

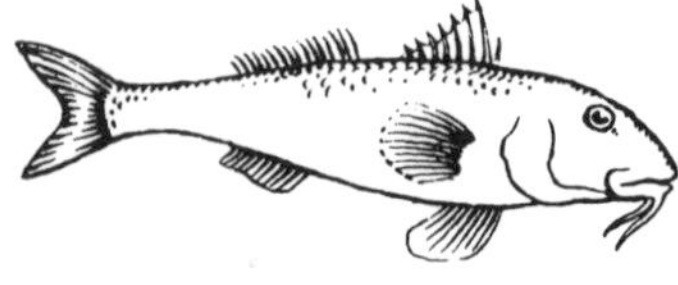

Name ______________________ Date ______________

116. State Oddities and Specialties—III

S
T
A
T
E

O
D
D
I
T
I
E
S

A
N
D

S
P
E
C
I
A
L
T
I
E
S

117. STATE ODDITIES AND SPECIALTIES—IV

Identify the state by its oddity or specialty.

ACROSS: ______________________________

1. Boasts the oldest women's college in America, Mount Holyoke
2. Chili originated here in the midnineteenth century
3. Boasts the first woman in America to own land, pay taxes, and practice law, Margaret Brent
4. Had the first written constitution
5. First Confederate state to be readmitted to the Union
6. Boasts the onion-growing capital of the world, Vidalia
7. Fastest-growing state
8. Location of the Badlands
9. State that is still 90 percent forest
10. 26 percent of this state's residents are Hispanic
11. Hosts North America's largest bird, the condor
12. Its Los Alamos National Laboratory developed the first atomic bomb
13. Nation's prime producer of milk, butter, and cheese
14. The "Lost Colony" location
15. Nation's largest producer of lobster, twenty million pounds per year
16. Driest of all the fifty states, receiving less than ten inches of rain a year
17. Location of the Liberty Bell
18. Over one hundred thousand Christmas trees are harvested here each year
19. Location of America's first drive-in movie theater, in 1933 near Camden
20. Boasts the tallest brick lighthouse in the country, 208 feet
21. Location of the country's largest known meteor crater
22. Only state with an official sport, medieval jousting
23. Swedish settlers built the first log cabins in the country here
24. Location of the largest rain forest in the continental United States
25. Nation's leading producer of cherries
26. First state to impose heavy fines for littering and prohibit the storage of nuclear waste
27. First in the world for its crayfish harvests

Name ______________________________ Date ____________________

117. State Oddities and Specialties—IV

1 S
2 T
3 A
4 T
5 E

6 O
7 D
8 D
9 I
10 T
11 I
12 E
13 S

14 A
15 N
16 D

17 S
18 P
19 E
20 C
21 I
22 A
23 L
24 T
25 I
26 E
27 S

118. STATE ODDITIES AND SPECIALTIES—V

Identify the state by its oddity or specialty.

ACROSS: ______________________________

1. The ice cream cone was invented here in 1904
2. Coal underlies nearly half of this state
3. Produces more rice than any other state
4. Host of NASA's headquarters
5. Last Confederate state to secede from the Union
6. First state to allow women to vote and hold office
7. Most rural state in the nation
8. Outside of Alaska, the federal government owns more land in this state than in any other state, 85 percent
9. A Cleveland disc jockey, Alan Freed, coined the term "rock and roll" here in the early 1950s
10. Location of the world's largest granite quarry
11. Location of the world's tallest trees, the coast redwoods
12. Boasts a full-scale replica of the Greek Parthenon
13. The ice cream soda was invented here in 1874
14. Location of the first school of forestry
15. This state is 80 percent farmland
16. Cattle outnumber people five to one in this state
17. Boasts the largest national park in the United States
18. Nation's catfish capital
19. Location of the U.S. Coast Guard Academy
20. Nearly all Marines are trained here at Parris Island
21. Manufactures nearly all the glass marbles made in the United States
22. Has more navigable water than any other state
23. Boasts the first zoo, pretzel, and cable car
24. Its lake has a higher saline content than either the Atlantic or Pacific Ocean
25. Boasts the world's last passenger pigeon, Martha, who died in 1914
26. Location of the nation's deepest lake
27. Leads the nation in the production of upholstered furniture

Name ______________________ Date ______________

118. State Oddities and Specialties—V

1 — S
2 — T
3 — A
4 — T
5 — E

6 — O
7 — D
8 — D
9 — I
10 — T
11 — I
12 — E
13 — S

14 — A
15 — N
16 — D

17 — S
18 — P
19 — E
20 — C
21 — I
22 — A
23 — L
24 — T
25 — I
26 — E
27 — S

119. STATE ODDITIES AND SPECIALTIES—VI

Identify the state by its oddity or specialty.

ACROSS:

1. Boasts the first root beer, circus, and pencils with erasers
2. Home of Casey Jones, the railroad engineer
3. Location of the world's most active volcano
4. Its state animal is the Morgan horse
5. Self-proclaimed poultry capital of the world at Gainesville
6. Home of the world's only museum devoted to first-edition postage stamps
7. Location of the nation's oldest city
8. Location of the first American factory
9. Its license plates depict a rider on a bucking horse
10. Its potatoes, brought from Roanoke Island by Sir Walter Raleigh, produced Ireland's first potato crop
11. Third-largest producer of potatoes in the United States
12. State originally claimed by the Dutch
13. Boasts the first lending library, weekly newspaper, and savings bank
14. Location of the first powered-airplane flight
15. Where "The Star-Spangled Banner" was written
16. Location of Mount Rushmore
17. Location of the highest peak in North America
18. Location of the assassination of Medgar Evers
19. Location of the U.S. Military Academy
20. Home of the nation's oldest active fishing port, Gloucester
21. Location of the Natural Bridge, one of the seven natural wonders of the world
22. Has the highest literacy rate in the nation
23. Boasts the first firefighting company, motion picture show, and commercial radio station
24. Produces 40 percent of America's coal
25. Has more Amish people, over sixty thousand, than any other state
26. First state to ban nonreturnable bottles and cans
27. Foremost manufacturer of steel

Name ______________________________ Date ______________

119. State Oddities and Specialties—VI

120. STATE PLACES TO VISIT—I

Identify the state by its tourist attractions.

ACROSS:

1. Acadian Village and the French Quarter
2. Custer Battlefield National Monument and Glacier National Park
3. Grandfather Mountain and Wright Brothers National Memorial
4. Peabody Museum and the USS *Nautilus* Memorial
5. Graceland and the Grand Ole Opry
6. Vicksburg National Military Park and DeSoto National Forest
7. Antietam National Battlefield and Fort McHenry
8. Boys Town and the Buffalo Bill ranch
9. The Biltmore Estate and Cape Hatteras National Seashore
10. Carlsbad Caverns National Park and Old Town
11. Gettysburg National Military Park and Independence Hall
12. The Alamo and Lyndon B. Johnson Space Center
13. Dinosaur National Monument and Pike's Peak
14. Lake Tahoe and Great Basin National Park
15. Henry Ford Museum and the National Cherry Festival
16. Glacier Bay National Park and Tongass Historical Museum and Totem Heritage Center
17. Walt Disney World and Everglades National Park
18. Zion National Park and Lake Powell

Name ______________________ Date ______________

120. State Places to Visit—I

1				S				

2 _ _ _ T _ _ _

3 _ _ _ _ _ _ A _ _ _ _ _ _

4 _ _ _ _ _ _ T _ _ _ _

5 _ _ _ _ E _ _ _ _

6 _ _ _ _ _ _ _ _ P _ _

7 _ _ _ _ L _ _ _

8 _ _ _ _ A _ _ _

9 _ _ _ _ _ C _ _ _ _ _ _ _

10 _ _ _ _ E _ _ _ _

11 _ _ _ _ S _ _ _ _ _ _ _

12 T _ _ _ _

13 _ _ _ O _ _ _ _

14 _ _ V _ _ _

15 _ _ _ _ I _ _ _

16 _ _ _ S _ _

17 _ _ _ _ I _ _

18 _ T _ _

121. STATE PLACES TO VISIT—II

Identify the state by its tourist attractions.

ACROSS: ______________________________

1. Valley Forge National Historical Park and Longwood Gardens
2. International Peace Garden and Theodore Roosevelt National Park
3. USS *Arizona* Memorial and Akaka Falls
4. Grand Coulee Dam and Mt. Rainier
5. Crater Lake National Park and Mt. Hood Wilderness Park
6. Franconia Notch State Park and Hampton Beach
7. Cherokee Heritage Center and the National Cowboy Hall of Fame
8. First White House of the Confederacy and Helen Keller's birthplace
9. Myrtle Beach and Swan Lake–Iris Gardens
10. Great Smoky Mountains and Museum of Appalachia
11. The Gateway Arch and Mark Twain National Forest
12. Mark Twain House and Dinosaur State Park
13. Devils Tower National Monument and Yellowstone National Park
14. Luray Caverns and Shenandoah National Park
15. Death Valley and Disneyland
16. Lookout Mountain and Cherokee National Forest
17. The Space Needle and Olympic National Park
18. Abraham Lincoln Birthplace National Historical Site and Cumberland Gap National Historical Park

Name ______________________________ Date ____________________

121. State Places to Visit—II

			1				S							
				2			T							
				3			A							
	4						T							
						5	E							
		6					P							
						7	L							
						8	A							
			9				C							
				10			E							
					11		S							
		12					T							
						13	O							
							14 V							
					15		I							
			16				S							
				17			I							
					18		T							

122. STATE PLACES TO VISIT—III

Identify the state by its tourist attractions.

ACROSS: ___

1. Hot Springs National Park and Fort Smith
2. Cape Cod National Seashore and Mt. Washington State Park
3. Redwood National Park and Mt. Whitney
4. Cumberland Gap National Historical Park and Fort Knox
5. Fort Ticonderoga and Lake Placid
6. Biloxi Shrimp Festival and Natchez Trace Parkway
7. Kennedy Space Center and Ringling Museum of Art
8. Shoshone Falls and Sun Valley Ski Resort
9. Yosemite National Park and Hearst Castle
10. Callaway Gardens and Stephen Foster State Park
11. Dorothy's house (*Wizard of Oz*) and the Eisenhower Center
12. Bryce Canyon National Park and Golden Spike National Historical Site
13. The Petrified Forest and Tombstone
14. Williamsburg Historic District and Blue Ridge Parkway
15. Lincoln Boyhood National Memorial and Wyandotte Caves
16. Ozark Mountains and Eureka Springs
17. Grand Canyon National Park and the Painted Desert
18. Yale University and the U.S. Coast Guard Academy

Name ______________________________ Date ____________________

122. State Places to Visit—III

1 S
2 T
3 A
4 T
5 E
6 P
7 L
8 A
9 C
10 E
11 S
12 T
13 O
14 V
15 I
16 S
17 I
18 T

123. STATE PLACES TO VISIT—IV

Identify the state by its tourist attractions.

ACROSS: ___

1. Little House on the Prairie and the Dalton Gang hideout and museum
2. National Bison Range and Giant Springs State Park
3. Tuskegee Institute National Historic Site and the world's largest space museum
4. Cherokee Indian Reservation and Carl Sandburg Home National Historic Site
5. American Museum of Science and Energy and the Hermitage
6. William Faulkner Home National Historic Landmark and Jefferson Davis's Home
7. Great Sand Dunes National Monument and Rocky Mountain National Park
8. Denali National Park and the Iditarod Sled Dog Race
9. Daniel Boone's grave and Churchill Downs racetrack
10. Aztec Ruins National Monument and Los Alamos Scientific Museum
11. Buffalo National River and Ozark Folk Center
12. Badlands National Park and Black Hills National Forest
13. London Bridge and the Apache Trail
14. Hoover Dam and Las Vegas
15. Haleakala National Park and Kalaupapa (leper colony)
16. The Tennis Hall of Fame and Slater Mill Historic Site
17. Fisherman's Wharf and Golden Gate Park
18. Sam Houston National Forest and Guadalupe Mountains National Park

Name ______________________________ Date ____________________

123. State Places to Visit—IV

1 _ _ _ S _ _
2 _ _ T _ _ _
3 _ A _ _ _ _
4 _ _ T _ _ _ _ _ _ _ _ _
5 _ _ _ E _ _ _ _
6 _ _ _ _ _ _ _ _ P _ _
7 _ L _ _ _ _ _
8 _ A _ _ _
9 _ _ _ _ C _ _
10 _ _ _ _ E _ _ _ _
11 _ _ _ _ _ S _ _
12 _ _ _ T _ _ _ _ _ _ _
13 _ _ _ _ O _ _
14 _ _ V _ _ _
15 _ _ _ _ I _
16 _ _ _ _ _ _ S _ _ _ _
17 _ _ _ I _ _ _ _ _ _
18 T _ _ _ _

124. STATE PLACES TO VISIT—V

Identify the state by its tourist attractions.

ACROSS:

1. The Mayo Clinic and Superior National Forest
2. Fort Sumter and Hilton Head Island
3. Warm Springs and Stone Mountain Park
4. National Space Hall of Fame and the Astrodome
5. Princeton University and Atlantic City Boardwalk
6. Hershey Park U.S.A. and American Golf Hall of Fame
7. Big Sur and Mission San Juan Capistrano
8. Hells Canyon and Craters of the Moon National Monument
9. Hiawatha National Forest and the Soo Locks
10. Lincoln Center and Franklin D. Roosevelt National Historic Site
11. Creole Nature Trail and Jean Lafitte National Historical Park
12. Paul Bunyan and Blue Ox Statue and Chippewa National Forest
13. Key West and the nation's oldest city
14. Green Mountain National Forest and Lake Champlain
15. Historic Fort Wayne and the University of Notre Dame
16. Harvard University and JFK National Historic Site
17. Nauvoo State Park and Lincoln Home State Memorial
18. Mount Rushmore National Memorial and Custer State Park

Name ______________________________ Date ____________________

124. State Places to Visit—V

1 S
2 T
3 A
4 T
5 E
6 P
7 L
8 A
9 C
10 E
11 S
12 T
13 O
14 V
15 I
16 S
17 I
18 T

125. STATE PLACES TO VISIT—VI

Identify the state by its tourist attractions.

ACROSS: ______________________________

1. Lake of the Ozarks and George Washington Carver National Monument
2. Mary Todd Lincoln's Home and Fort Boonesborough
3. Strategic Air Command Museum and Omaha Indian Pow Wow
4. The Alamo and Padre Island National Seashore
5. Carnegie Hall and Central Park
6. Lake Winnipesaukee and Robert Frost's farm
7. The U.S. Air Force Academy and the Denver Mint
8. The U.S. Naval Academy and Johns Hopkins University
9. Paul Revere's Home and the USS *Constitution*
10. Jekyll Island and the Okefenokee Swamp
11. Edison National Historic Site and Washington Crossing State Park
12. Flathead Lake and Virginia City
13. Palm Springs and Sequoia National Park
14. Allegheny National Forest and Betsy Ross house
15. Knott's Berry Farm and Lion Country Safari
16. Harry S Truman Library and Mark Twain boyhood home
17. Sea World and Cypress Gardens
18. Plymouth Rock and Cape Cod National Seashore

Name ______________________ Date ______________

125. State Places to Visit—VI

							1			S							
							2			T							
						3				A							
										4 T							
									5	E							
			6							P							
								7		L							
				8						A							
				9						C							
									10	E							
			11							S							
							12			T							
				13						O							
		14								V							
							15			I							
							16			S							
						17				I							
18										T							

Name ______________________________ Date ____________________

126. STATE COLLEGES AND UNIVERSITIES—I

Identify the state by its college or university.

ACROSS: ____

1. Clemson
2. Columbia
3. Bowie State
4. Lehigh
5. Baylor
6. Old Dominion
7. King
8. Bethel
9. Purdue
10. DePaul
11. Brown
12. Loyola
13. Bates
14. Notre Dame
15. Villanova
16. Vanderbilt
17. Shaw
18. Dartmouth
19. Pepperdine
20. Yale
21. Oberlin
22. Rice
23. Tulane

Name ______________________________ Date ____________________

127. STATE COLLEGES AND UNIVERSITIES—II

C O L L E G E S A N D U N I V E R S I T I E S

Identify the state by its college or university.

ACROSS: ______________________________

1. Elon
2. Cornell
3. Johns Hopkins
4. Tuskegee
5. Rutgers
6. Morehouse
7. Fordham
8. Radcliffe
9. Duke
10. James Madison
11. Notre Dame
12. Harvard
13. Iona
14. Washington and Lee
15. Temple
16. Seton Hall
17. Vassar
18. Fisk
19. Drake
20. Louisville
21. Wilberforce
22. Bard
23. Princeton

Name ______________________________ Date ______________________

128. STATE WORDSEARCH

```
W A S M A I N N E W H A M P S H I R E A A T
I R S O I D A H O O S A R A W O I T I L T E
S A M C O N N E C T I C U T X H Y N U A O N
C N I I D F N H L N P A N O Z I R A V B K N
W I C X A W E E E Q O K L A H O M A Y A A E
E L H E R D S A S A X E T N F O R D K M D I
S O I M O F E G N O T G N I H S A W C A H N
T R G W L I K L A S T O L R I B I R U A T D
V A A E O S R M A S S A C H U S E T T S R I
I C N N C E O R D W C H A C C O O N N E O A
R H K A N R Y S A S A L A O K U T E E A N N
G T E X E M W I S T I R N E B T E W K A D A
I R H G M O E T U T A S E X Y H A J A M N E
N O O H A I N I G R I V I R G C O E J W A S
I N E V A D S O U N G S A S N A K R A L L G
A I N A V L Y S N N E P L T T R I S O U S T
A L A S S O U T I D E H A O H O I E A S I R
M I S S I I X M A S S V K A U L A Y U R E E
H A W A I I O W I S S A A L A I O W U A D E
R K N E V Y A N O R D I S D O N S O D S O S
A S I A W A I I I H A W P E A A S I S L H S
C A L L T E G E T L O U I P S S R H A C R E
I R F A R N R U T A L K E N I O K L A N E N
O B I S O U O R E G O I A M L M A R Y L A N
K E N K I S E M A I N K A F L O R I S A E E
O N A A L A G D N A L Y R A M V E R M O N T
```

Hidden in the puzzle are the names of all fifty states. Find the name of each state and write it in the blank provided. Answers can be found horizontally, vertically, diagonally, and backward.

1. ____________ 14. ____________ 27. ____________ 40. ____________
2. ____________ 15. ____________ 28. ____________ 41. ____________
3. ____________ 16. ____________ 29. ____________ 42. ____________
4. ____________ 17. ____________ 30. ____________ 43. ____________
5. ____________ 18. ____________ 31. ____________ 44. ____________
6. ____________ 19. ____________ 32. ____________ 45. ____________
7. ____________ 20. ____________ 33. ____________ 46. ____________
8. ____________ 21. ____________ 34. ____________ 47. ____________
9. ____________ 22. ____________ 35. ____________ 48. ____________
10. ____________ 23. ____________ 36. ____________ 49. ____________
11. ____________ 24. ____________ 37. ____________ 50. ____________
12. ____________ 25. ____________ 38. ____________
13. ____________ 26. ____________ 39. ____________

Name ______________________________ Date ____________________

129. STATE CAPITAL WORDSEARCH

```
E D M A R H A R R I S B U R G R I C H M E
B E L L I V H S A N N O S K C A J O M H C
K N E W B I S M A R C K N A S H U O H A N
S V X H S U B M U L O C E F D E N V E R E
C E Y O J I T O R J E K A K A T E O L T D
R O T N E M A R C A S M D C G U A L E F I
I K I O S P L H E X I N E O H P U S N O V
J L C L I S L A L L O N M R V T S I O R O
O A N U L L A L A B B E T E N E P L T D R
M H O L O L H S A N R L A L A Y R O S A P
P O S U P Y A E I Y C I T T A T I P E I C
A M R R A S S T L N I N L T O I N A L P O
R A E L N O S S R E O A A I I C G N R M L
E C F U N U E T O R N T N L X N F A A Y U
U I F R A K E P O T Y A S Z R O I I H L M
I T E R A S K A A S E N I O M S E D C O B
Z Y J S O N R U S U M O N I B R L N O Y I
D D I E L U K L A N G O G I X A D I N P A
N N M F E I F F O R D U P N A C A A C O E
O O B A T O N R O U G E S O N E B R O E N
M M O T A N A C I R E S A T I L L E R S N
H H O N O L U L O S T A R N A D E R D I E
C C R A S H G I E L A R I E T E E S I T Y
I I A S H A R R I S N I O R C I T Y S I E
R E I L E P T N O M U X P T P O M M E R H
A S A L T L A K E C I T Y N O S I D A M C
```

Hidden in the puzzle are the names of the capital cities of all fifty states. In the blank provided, write the name of the correct capital by the name of the state. Answers can be found horizontally, vertically, diagonally, and backward.

____________ Alabama

____________ Alaska

____________ Arizona

____________ Arkansas

____________ California

____________ Colorado

____________ Connecticut

____________ Delaware

____________ Florida

____________ Georgia

____________ Hawaii

____________ Idaho

____________ Illinois

____________ Indiana

____________ Iowa

____________ Kansas

____________ Kentucky

____________ Louisiana

____________ Maine

____________ Maryland

____________ Massachusetts

____________ Michigan

____________ Minnesota

____________ Mississippi

____________ Missouri

____________ Montana

____________ Nebraska

____________ Nevada

____________ New Hampshire

____________ New Jersey

____________ New Mexico

____________ New York

____________ North Carolina

____________ North Dakota

____________ Ohio

____________ Oklahoma

____________ Oregon

____________ Pennsylvania

____________ Rhode Island

____________ South Carolina

____________ South Dakota

____________ Tennessee

____________ Texas

____________ Utah

____________ Vermont

____________ Virginia

____________ Washington

____________ West Virginia

____________ Wisconsin

____________ Wyoming

Name ________________________ Date ________________

130. State Silhouettes

1. ________________
2. ________________
3. ________________
4. ________________
5. ________________
6. ________________
7. ________________
8. ________________
9. ________________
10. ________________
11. ________________
12. ________________
13. ________________
14. ________________
15. ________________
16. ________________
17. ________________
18. ________________
19. ________________
20. ________________
21. ________________
22. ________________
23. ________________
24. ________________
25. ________________
26. ________________
27. ________________
28. ________________
29. ________________
30. ________________
31. ________________
32. ________________
33. ________________
34. ________________
35. ________________
36. ________________
37. ________________
38. ________________
39. ________________
40. ________________
41. ________________
42. ________________
43. ________________
44. ________________
45. ________________
46. ________________
47. ________________
48. ________________
49. ________________
50. ________________

130. STATE SILHOUETTES

Identify the state by its shape.

Name ______________________________ Date ____________________

131. State Flags

Identify the state by its flag.

1. ______________________
2. ______________________
3. ______________________
4. ______________________
5. ______________________
6. ______________________
7. ______________________
8. ______________________
9. ______________________
10. ______________________
11. ______________________
12. ______________________
13. ______________________
14. ______________________
15. ______________________
16. ______________________
17. ______________________
18. ______________________
19. ______________________
20. ______________________
21. ______________________
22. ______________________
23. ______________________
24. ______________________
25. ______________________
26. ______________________
27. ______________________
28. ______________________
29. ______________________
30. ______________________
31. ______________________
32. ______________________
33. ______________________
34. ______________________
35. ______________________
36. ______________________
37. ______________________
38. ______________________
39. ______________________
40. ______________________
41. ______________________
42. ______________________
43. ______________________
44. ______________________
45. ______________________
46. ______________________
47. ______________________
48. ______________________
49. ______________________
50. ______________________

131. STATE FLAGS

STATE INFORMATION AGENCIES

ALABAMA BUREAU OF TOURISM AND TRAVEL
532 South Perry Street
Montgomery, Alabama 36104
Telephone: 800-ALABAMA

DIVISION OF TOURISM
P.O. Box E
Juneau, Alaska 99811
Telephone: 907-465-2010

ARIZONA OFFICE OF TOURISM
1100 West Washington
Phoenix, Arizona 85007
Telephone: 602-542-8687

ARKANSAS DEPARTMENT OF PARKS AND TOURISM
1 Capitol Mall
Little Rock, Arkansas 72201
Telephone: 501-682-7777

CALIFORNIA OFFICE OF TOURISM
801 K Street, Suite 1600
Sacramento, California 95814
Telephone: 916-322-2881

COLORADO TOURISM BOARD
1625 Broadway, Suite 1700
Denver, Colorado 80202
Telephone: 303-592-5410

CONNECTICUT DEPARTMENT OF ECONOMIC DEVELOPMENT
865 Brook Street
Rocky Hill, Connecticut 06067
Telephone: 800-282-6863

DELAWARE TOURISM OFFICE
99 Kings Highway, Box 1401
Dover, Delaware 19903
Telephone: 800-441-8846

FLORIDA DEPARTMENT OF COMMERCE
Division of Tourism
126 West Van Buren Street
Tallahassee, Florida 32399
Telephone: 904-487-1462

GEORGIA DEPARTMENT OF INDUSTRY, TRADE, AND TOURISM
P.O. Box 1776
Atlanta, Georgia 30301
Telephone: 404-656-3590

HAWAII VISITORS BUREAU
2270 Kalakaua Avenue, Suite 801
Honolulu, Hawaii 96815
Telephone: 808-923-1811

VACATIONLAND—IDAHO
Idaho Travel Council
Room 108, Statehouse
Boise, Idaho 83720
Telephone: 800-635-7820

ILLINOIS DEPARTMENT OF COMMERCE AND COMMUNITY AFFAIRS
Division of Tourism
620 East Adams Street
Springfield, Illinois 62701
Telephone: 217-782-7139

INDIANA DEPARTMENT OF COMMERCE
Tourism Development Division
1 North Capitol, Suite 700
Indianapolis, Indiana 46204
Telephone: 800-782-3775

IOWA DEPARTMENT OF ECONOMIC DEVELOPMENT
Division of Tourism
200 East Grand Avenue
Des Moines, Iowa 50309
Telephone: 800-345-IOWA

KANSAS DEPARTMENT OF COMMERCE
Travel and Tourism Division
400 Southwest 8th Street, 5th floor
Topeka, Kansas 66603
Telephone: 800-2-KANSAS

KENTUCKY DEPARTMENT OF TRAVEL DEVELOPMENT
500 Mero Street
Frankfort, Kentucky 40601
Telephone: 800-225-TRIP

STATE DEPARTMENT OF CULTURE, RECREATION, AND TOURISM
P.O.Box 94291
Baton Rouge, Louisiana 70804
Telephone: 800-33-GUMBO

THE MAINE PUBLICITY BUREAU
97 Winthrop Street
Hallowell, Maine 04347
Telephone: 207-289-6070

MARYLAND OFFICE OF TOURISM DEVELOPMENT
217 East Redwood Street
Baltimore, Maryland 21202
Telephone: 301–333–6611

MASSACHUSETTS OFFICE OF TRAVEL AND TOURISM
100 Cambridge Street, 13th floor
Boston, Massachusetts 02202
Telephone: 617–727–3201

MICHIGAN TRAVEL BUREAU
Department of Commerce
P.O. Box 30226
Lansing, Michigan 48909
Telephone: 800–543–2–YES

MINNESOTA OFFICE OF TOURISM
250 Skyway Level
375 Jackson Street
St. Paul, Minnesota 55101
Telephone: 800–657–3700

DIVISION OF TOURISM DEVELOPMENT
P.O. Box 22825
Jackson, Mississippi 39205
Telephone: 800–647–2290

MISSOURI DIVISION OF TOURISM
P.O. Box 1055
Jefferson City, Missouri 65102
Telephone: 800–877–1234

MONTANA DEPARTMENT OF COMMERCE
Travel Montana
1424 9th Avenue
Helena, Montana 59620
Telephone: 800–541–1447

NEBRASKA DIVISION OF TRAVEL AND TOURISM
P.O. Box 94666
Lincoln, Nebraska 68509
Telephone: 800–228–4307

COMMISSION ON TOURISM
Capitol Complex
Carson City, Nevada 89710
Telephone: 702–687–4322

NEW HAMPSHIRE OFFICE OF VACATION TRAVEL
P.O. Box 856
Concord, New Hampshire 03302
Telephone: 603–271–2343

NEW JERSEY DIVISION OF TRAVEL AND TOURISM
20 West State Street, CN–826
Trenton, New Jersey 08625
Telephone: 609–292–2470

NEW MEXICO DEPARTMENT OF TRAVEL AND TOURISM
Joseph M. Montoya State Building
1100 St. Francis Drive
Santa Fe, New Mexico 87503
Telephone: 800–545–2040

NEW YORK DEPARTMENT OF ECONOMIC DEVELOPMENT
Division of Tourism
1 Commerce Plaza
Albany, New York 12245
Telephone: 518–474–4116

NORTH CAROLINA TRAVEL AND TOURISM DIVISION
430 North Salisbury Street
Raleigh, North Carolina 27603
Telephone: 800–847–4862

NORTH DAKOTA TOURISM PROMOTION
604 East Boulevard
Bismarck, North Dakota 58505
Telephone: 701–224–2525

OHIO OFFICE OF TRAVEL AND TOURISM
P.O. Box 1001
Columbus, Ohio 43266
Telephone: 800–BUCKEYE

OKLAHOMA TOURISM AND RECREATION DEPARTMENT
505 Will Rogers Building
Oklahoma City, Oklahoma 73105
Telephone: 405–521–2406

OREGON TOURISM DIVISION
775 Summer Street NE
Salem, Oregon 97310
Telephone: 800–547–7842

DEPARTMENT OF COMMERCE
Bureau of Travel Marketing
Forum Building, Room 453
Harrisburg, Pennsylvania 17120
Telephone: 717–787–5453

DEPARTMENT OF ECONOMIC DEVELOPMENT
Tourism Division
7 Jackson Walkway
Providence, Rhode Island 02903
Telephone: 401–277–2601

South Carolina Division of Tourism
P.O. Box 71
Columbia, South Carolina 29202
Telephone: 803–734–0235

South Dakota Department of Tourism
711 East Wells Avenue
Pierre, South Dakota 57501
Telephone: 800–843–1930

Department of Tourist Development
P.O. Box 23170
Nashville, Tennessee 37202
Telephone: 615–741–2158

Texas Department of Commerce
Tourism Division
P.O. Box 12728
Austin, Texas 78711
Telephone: 512–462–9191

Utah Travel Council
Council Hall
Capitol Hill
Salt Lake City, Utah 84114
Telephone: 801–538–1030

Vermont Travel Division
134 State Street
Montpelier, Vermont 05602
Telephone: 802–828–3236

Virginia Division of Tourism
1021 East Cary Street
Richmond, Virginia 23219
Telephone: 804–786–4484

Washington State Tourism Division
101 General Administration Building
Olympia, Washington 98504
Telephone: 206–753–5600

Travel West Virginia
2101 Washington Street East
Charleston, West Virginia 25305
Telephone: 800–225–5982

Wisconsin Department of Development
Division of Tourism
Box 7606
Madison, Wisconsin 53702
Telephone: 608–266–2161

Division of Tourism
I–25 at College Drive
Cheyenne, Wyoming 82002
Telephone: 307–777–7777

Answer Key

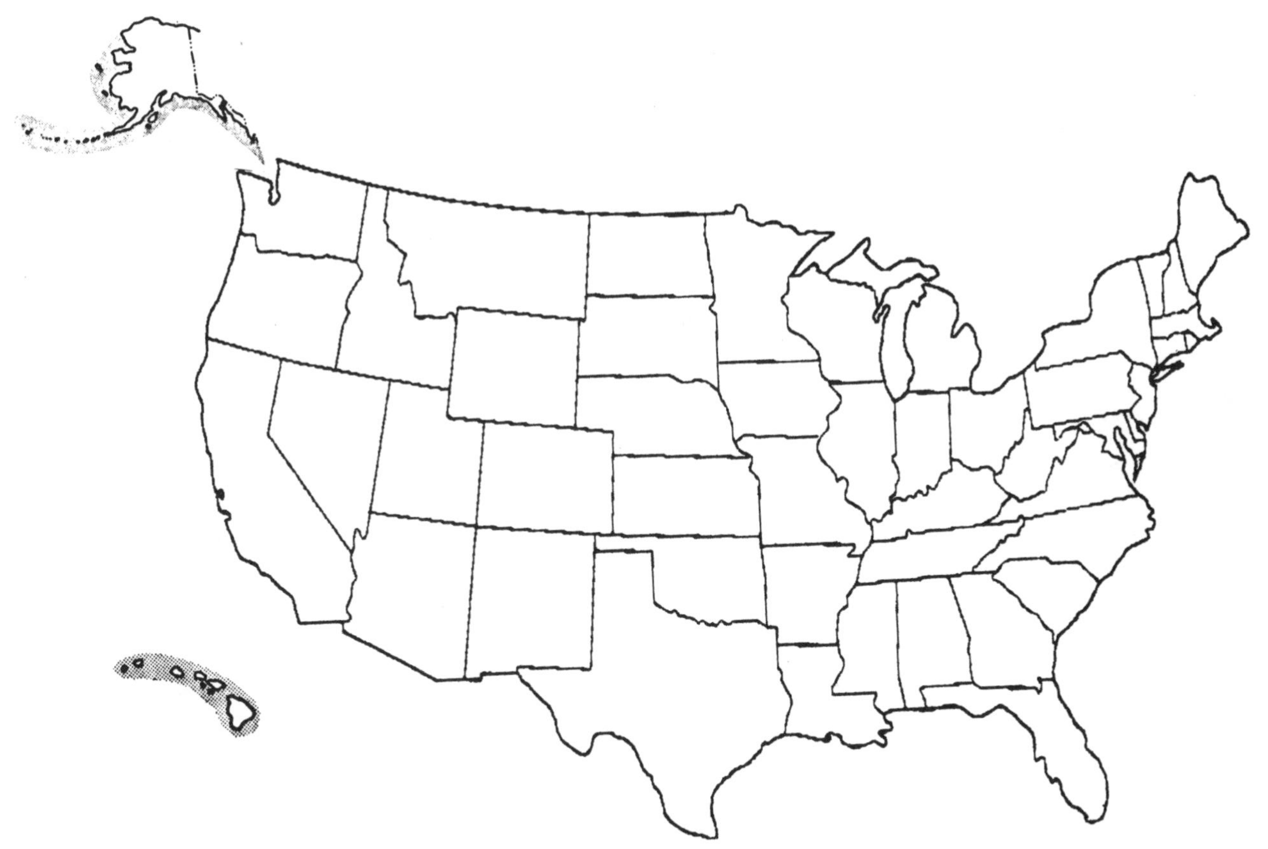

1. The Original Thirteen States—I

1. DELAWARE
2. RHODE ISLAND
3. CONNECTICUT
4. NEW HAMPSHIRE
5. SOUTH CAROLINA
6. NEW JERSEY
7. MASSACHUSETTS
8. PENNSYLVANIA
9. VIRGINIA
10. NEW YORK
11. MARYLAND
12. GEORGIA
13. NORTH CAROLINA

2. The Original Thirteen States—II

1. PO**T**OMAC
2. POCA**H**ONTAS
3. NEWJ**E**RSEY
4. BAC**O**N
5. CHA**R**LESTON
6. VIRG**I**NIA
7. NARRA**G**ANSETT
8. WILL**I**AMS
9. ALBA**N**Y
10. DEL**A**WARE
11. MARY**L**AND
12. CA**T**HOLICS
13. S**H**AYS
14. BALT**I**MORE
15. HA**R**TFORD
16. DU**T**CH
17. SW**E**DES
18. QUAK**E**RS
19. SAVA**N**NAH
20. MAS**S**ACHUSETTS
21. JAMES**T**OWN
22. APPAL**A**CHIANS
23. PLYMOU**T**H
24. CONN**E**CTICUT
25. RHODEI**S**LAND

3. The Original Thirteen States—III

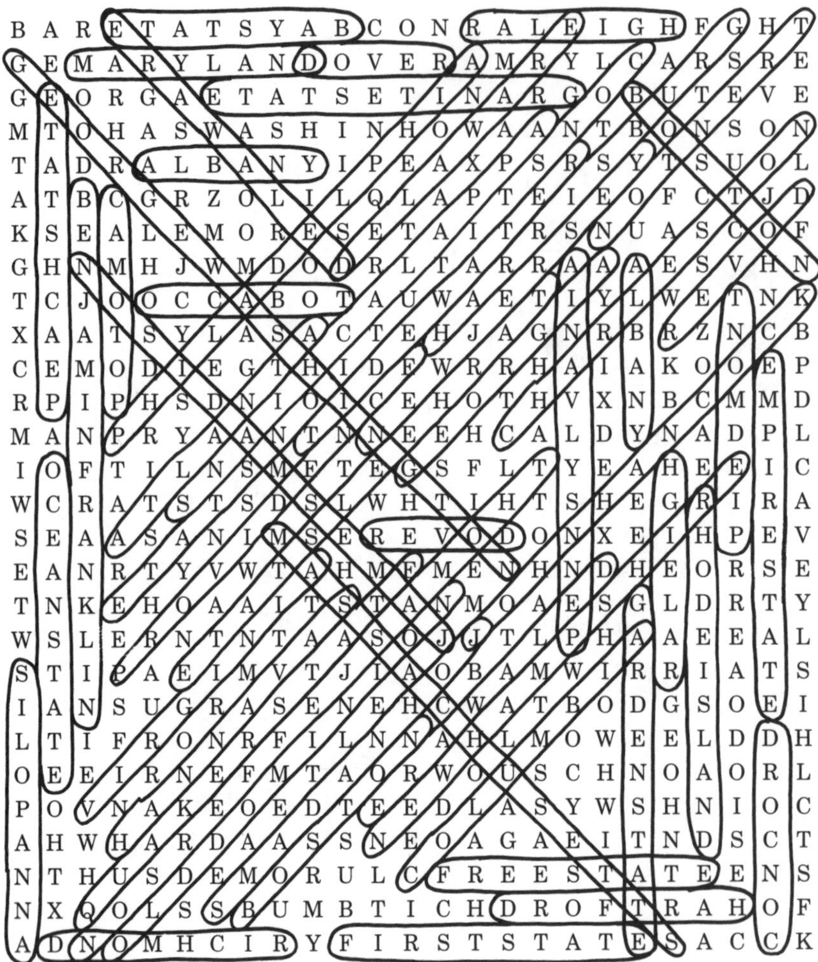

1. James Madison
2. Potomac
3. Delaware
4. Pennsylvania
5. Constitution State
6. Richmond
7. Savannah
8. Atlanta
9. Empire State
10. tobacco
11. Columbia
12. Maryland
13. First State
14. Massachusetts
15. George Washington
16. Providence
17. Tarheel State
18. Dover
19. Thomas Jefferson
20. New Hampshire
21. Harrisburg
22. Peach State
23. Delaware
24. New Jersey
25. Old Dominion
26. Raleigh
27. John Hancock
28. Philadelphia
29. Free State
30. Piedmont
31. Albany
32. Virginia
33. Quaker State
34. Hartford
35. Benjamin Franklin
36. Trenton
37. Bay State
38. John Adams
39. Appalachians
40. Ocean State
41. Concord
42. Georgia
43. Granite State
44. Charleston
45. tidewater
46. Boston
47. Delaware
48. Rhode Island
49. Garden State
50. Annapolis

4. The Louisiana Purchase

1. PLATTE
2. MERIWETHERLEWIS
3. THOMASJEFFERSON
4. ZEBULONPIKE
5. YELLOWSTONE
6. STLOUIS
7. ROBERTLIVINGSTON
8. MISSISSIPPI
9. WILLIAMCLARK
10. LASALLE
11. ARKANSAS
12. SACAJAWEA
13. NAPOLEON
14. MISSOURI
15. YORK
16. ROCKIES
17. SHOSHONE
18. FRANCE
19. JAMESMONROE
20. NEWORLEANS

5. The Western Frontier

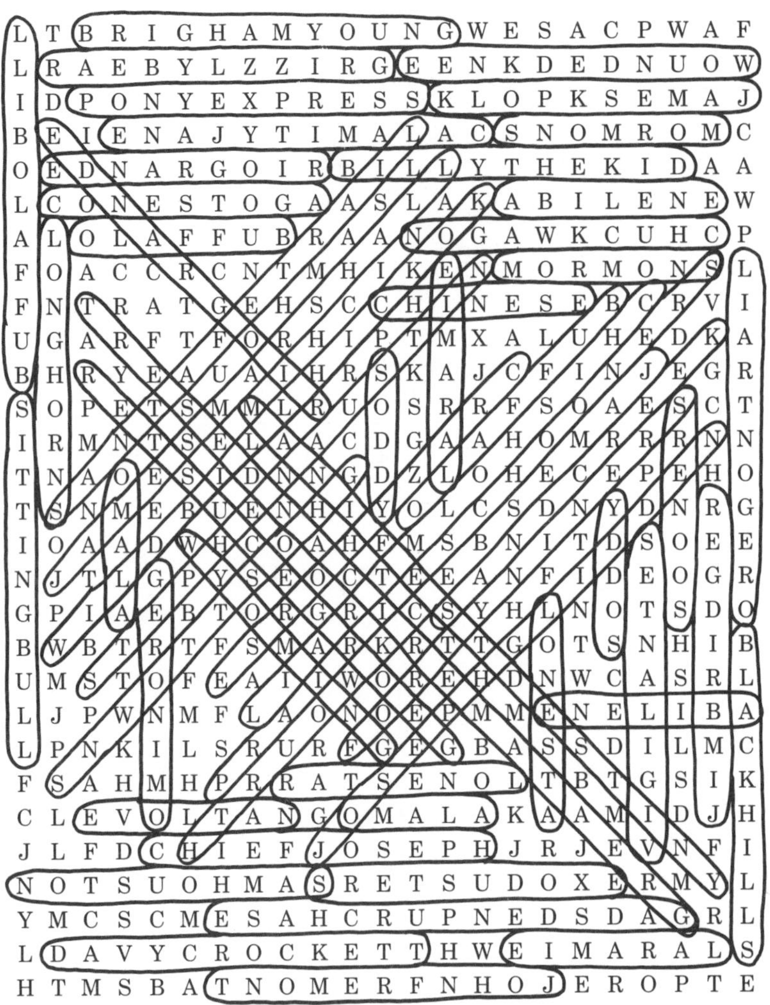

1. vigilantes
2. Wyoming
3. chuck wagon
4. Great American Desert
5. Chinese
6. Sand Creek
7. Chief Joseph
8. Chisholm Trail
9. Geronimo
10. prairie schooners
11. Jim Bridger
12. Manifest Destiny
13. ghost towns
14. James Beckwourth
15. Brigham Young
16. John Fremont
17. longhorns
18. Nat Love
19. exodusters
20. Abilene
21. Billy the Kid
22. Sooners
23. Pony Express
24. Wild Bill Hickok
25. Soddy
26. Joseph Glidden
27. forty-niners
28. George Custer
29. buffalo
30. Black Hills
31. Crazy Horse
32. Wounded Knee
33. Calamity Jane
34. Sitting Bull
35. Buffalo Bill
36. Alamo
37. Oregon Trail
38. James Marshall
39. grizzly bear
40. Stephen Austin
41. Gadsden Purchase
42. Laramie
43. Sam Houston
44. Rio Grande
45. Santa Fe Trail
46. Mormons
47. Conestoga
48. Davy Crockett
49. James K. Polk
50. Lone Star

6. The Civil War—States of the Union

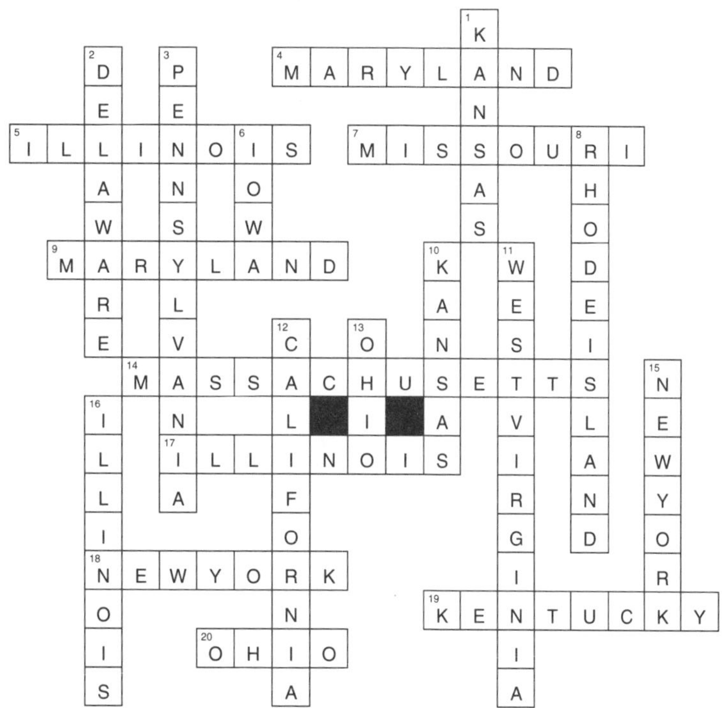

7. The Civil War—States of the Confederacy

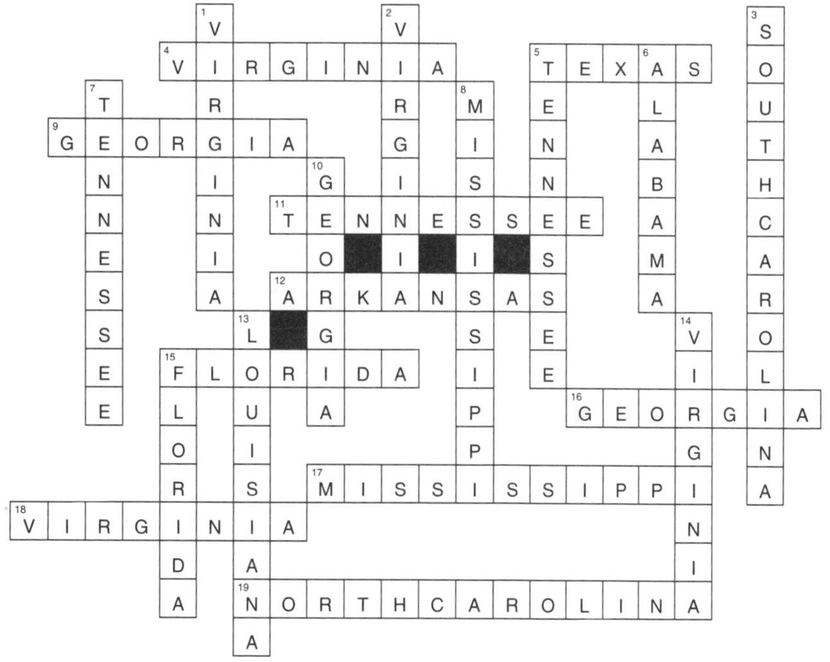

8. The Civil War

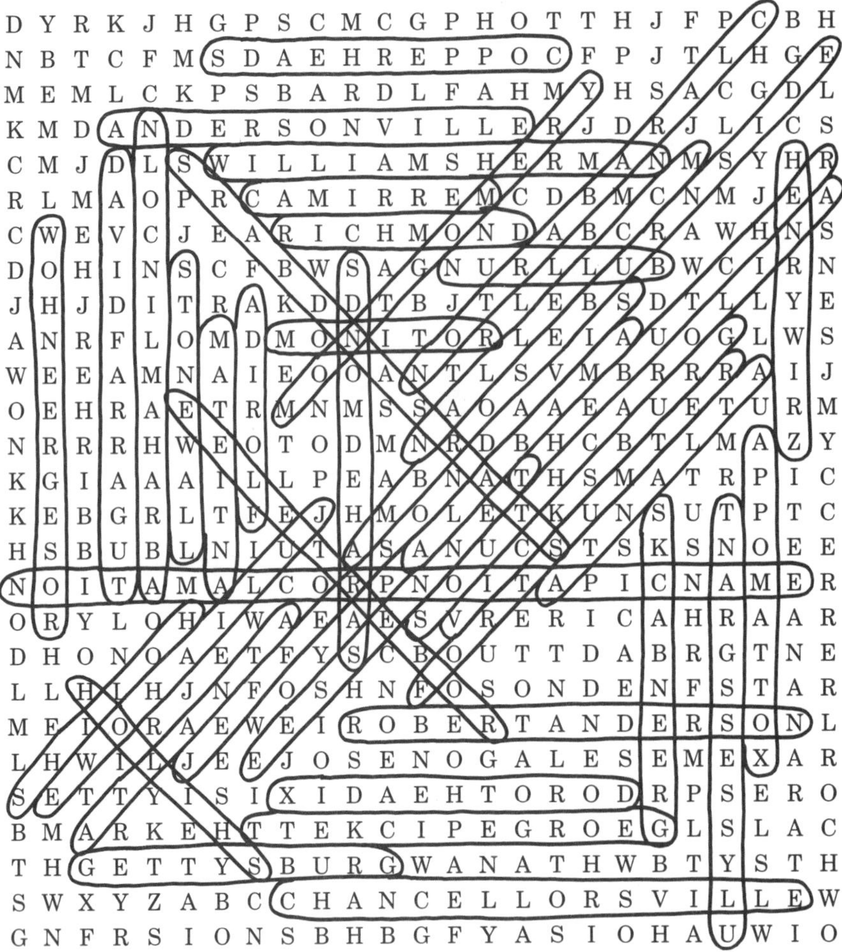

1. Fort Sumter
2. Starts and Bars
3. Jefferson Davis
4. Abraham Lincoln
5. South Carolina
6. Tennessee
7. Robert Anderson
8. Montgomery
9. Bull Run
10. Antietam
11. Robert E. Lee
12. Ulysses S. Grant
13. Stonewall
14. greenbacks
15. *Monitor*
16. *Merrimac*
17. David Farragut
18. William Sherman
19. Julia Howe
20. Dorothea Dix
21. Clara Barton
22. Rose Greenhow
23. Sarah Edmonds
24. Ambrose Burnside
25. Chancellorsville
26. Gettysburg
27. Appomattox
28. *Alabama*
29. Emancipation Proclamation
30. Andersonville
31. George Pickett
32. The Butcher
33. Richmond
34. Vicksburg
35. McClellan
36. Shiloh
37. *Florida*
38. Atlanta
39. Henry Wirz
40. Copperheads

9. The New England States—I

1 VERMONT
2 CONNECTICUT
3 RHODE ISLAND
4 MAINE
5 MASSACHUSETTS
6 RHODE ISLAND
7 VERMONT
8 MAINE
9 MAINE
10 MASSACHUSETTS
11 CONNECTICUT
12 CONNECTICUT
13 VERMONT
14 MAINE
15 NEW
16 MAINE
17 MAINE
19 MAINE
19 VERMONT
20 MAINE
21 NEW HAMPSHIRE
22 MASSACHUSETTS
23 NEW HAMPSHIRE
24 MASSACHUSETTS
25 NEW HAMPSHIRE
26 MAINE
27 MAINE
28 VERMONT
29 MAINE
30 VERMONT
31 MASSACHUSETTS
32 MAINE
33 MAINE
34 NEW HAMPSHIRE
35 MAINE
36 MAINE
37 VERMONT
38 MAINE
39 CONNECTICUT
40 ISLAND
41 MAINE
42 RHODE ISLAND
43 MASSACHUSETTS

10. The New England States—II

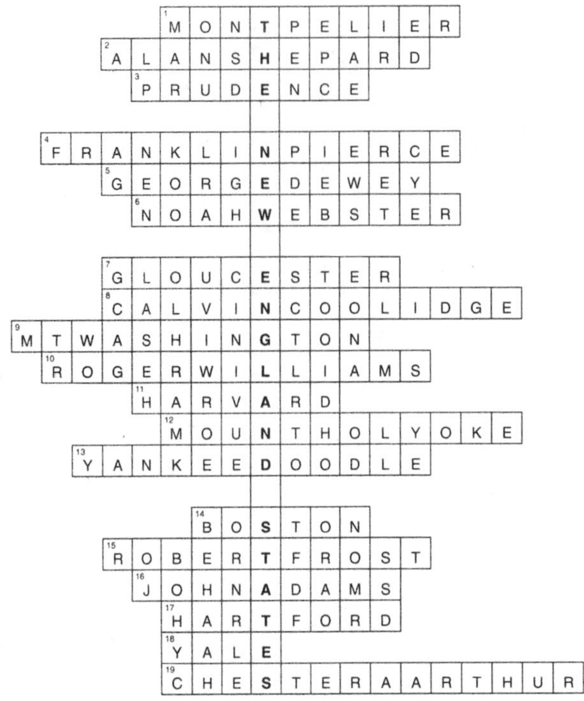

11. The New England States—III

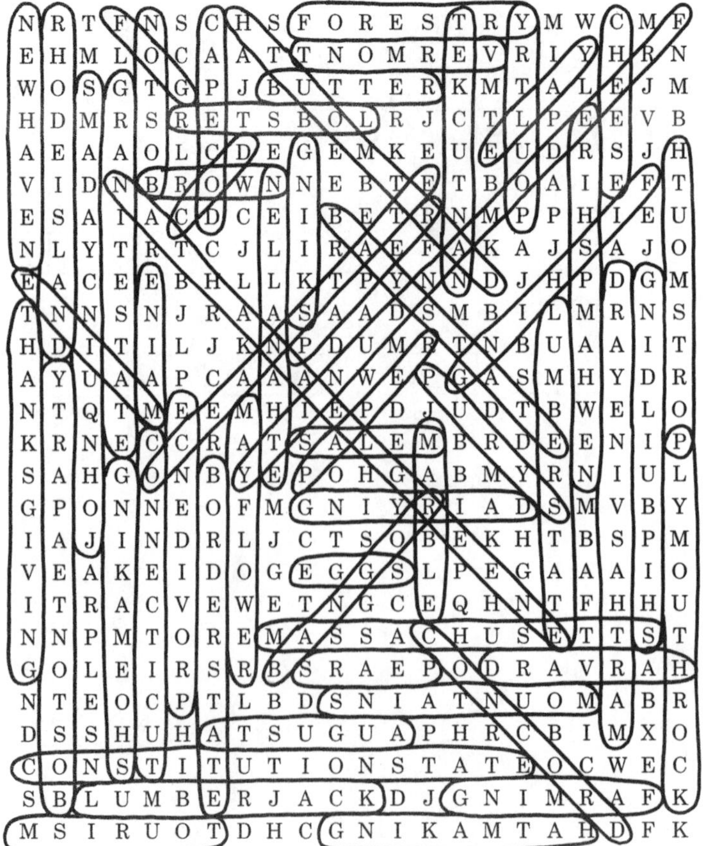

12. Connecticut

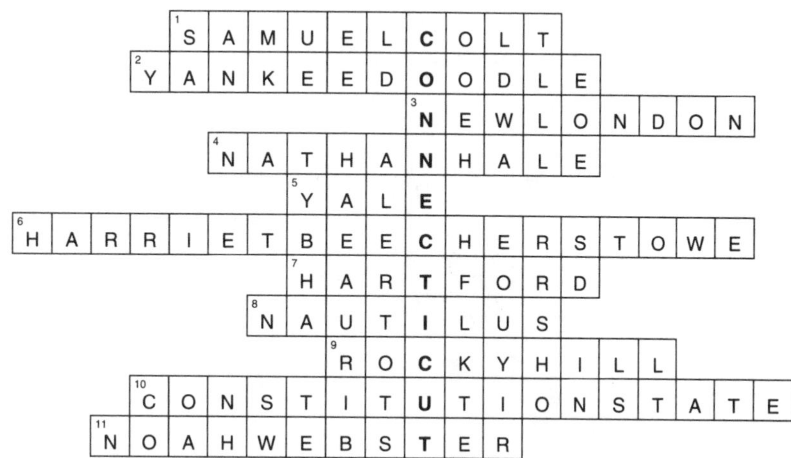

13. Maine

1 LUMBERSTATE
2 ACADIA
3 CHICKADEE
4 LONGFELLOW
5 PINETREESTATE

14. Massachusetts

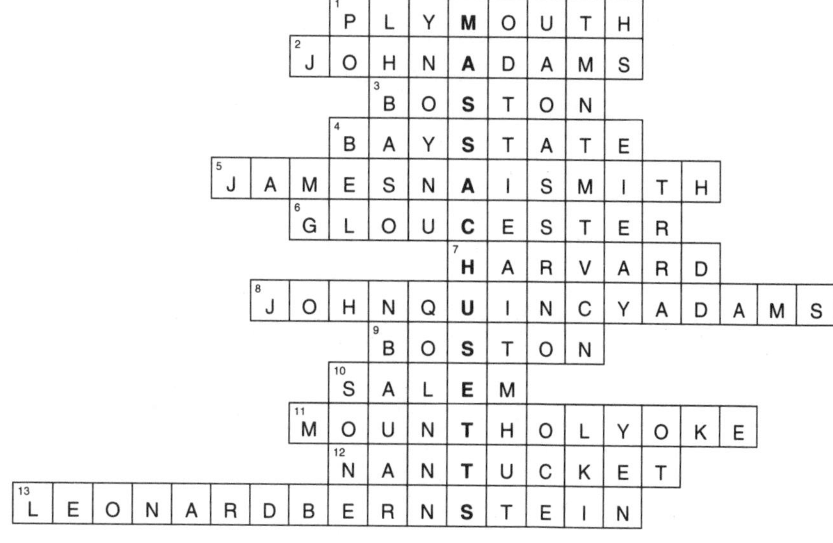

15. New Hampshire

1. CONCORD
2. WHITEBIRCH
3. DANIELWEBSTER
4. MANCHESTER
5. GRANITESTATE
6. DARTMOUTH
7. PURPLELILAC
8. ANDROSCOGGIN
9. ALANSHEPARD
10. FRANKLINPIERCE
11. ROBERTFROST
12. PURPLEFINCH

16. Rhode Island

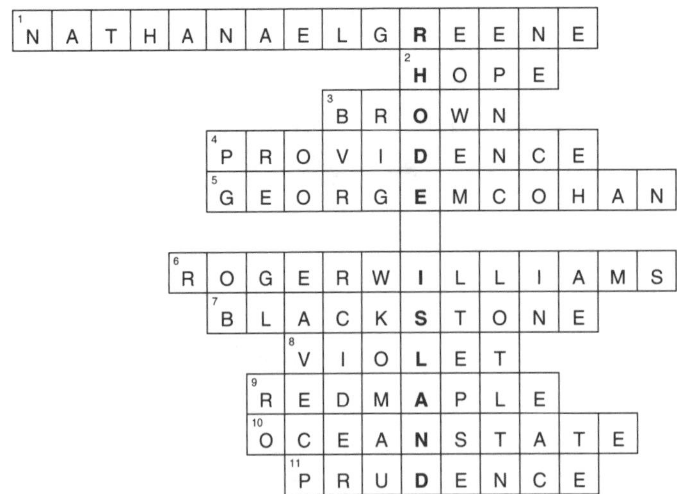

17. Vermont

1. REDCLOVER
2. GEORGEDEWEY
3. CHESTERAARTHUR
4. FREEDOMANDUNITY
5. CALVINCOOLIDGE
6. ETHANALLEN
7. MONTPELIER

18. The Middle Atlantic States—I

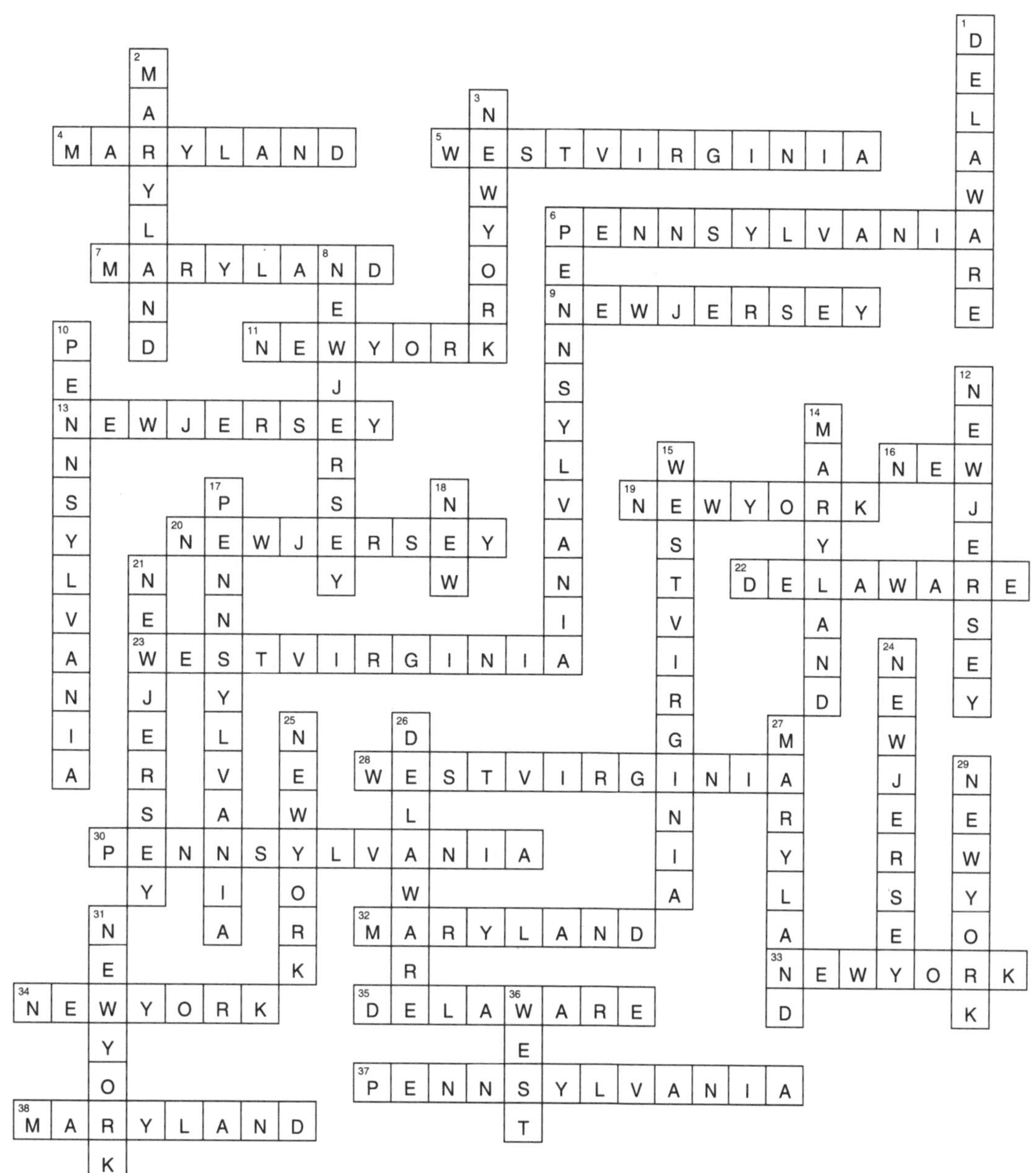

19. The Middle Atlantic States—II

1. NEWAMS**T**ERDAM
2. FORTMC**H**ENRY
3. GARD**E**NSTATE
4. THURGOOD**M**ARSHALL
5. FRANKL**I**NROOSEVELT
6. UNITE**D**NATIONS
7. PHILA**D**ELPHIA
8. ROBERTFU**L**TON
9. BAB**E**RUTH
10. MOUNT**A**INSTATE
11. WES**T**POINT
12. STATUEOF**L**IBERTY
13. MISS**A**MERICA
14. BENJAMI**N**FRANKLIN
15. KEYS**T**ONESTATE
16. ER**I**E
17. GROVER**C**LEVELAND
18. PEARL**S**BUCK
19. COOPERS**T**OWN
20. MANH**A**TTAN
21. PRINCE**T**ON
22. THOMAS**E**DISON
23. WALL**S**TREET

20. The Middle Atlantic States—III

```
D N A L Y R A M F L L O C E A N C I T Y S
B N E J Q N T S I L O P A N N A S H R L J
E E L K U C A E E A M N N L R D O V E R L
G M I E A J I B T O E E G E M B J R V L B
R W P R K R Y R L C W B K I O T K E I A H
O E Y I E T O L B A U A R K S R C V R K A
F S N E R Y E T R F U M E L O L F O N E I
Y T A E S E C K F Q G N I Y R I A D O P N
E V B R T E S A D E L A W A R E R N S L A
L I L S A A L T D S R E K A U Q M D D A V
L R A S T O A M A A N G N I H S I F U C L
A G T H E F I R S T S T A T E M N E H I Y
V I C Y E S R E J W E N T R O Y G D J D S
P N E I T H A C A Y R T L U O P M C T K N
C I N G N I L E E H W S A R L A H H C G N
C A T S K I L L S N Y N N C T D E A W R E
A P R T C O A L O R O O T E K R D R E U P
M O A E S O K T A T T M I N I N G L S B R
O T L E C B N C N N A T C E O Y S E T S I
T O P L W E U A E L N K C R I O T S P Y N
O M A E R S R R B A L T I M O R E T O T C
P A R T E C T X G I V D T M O T E O I T E
V C K J S C S D C H A C Y Y G E L N N E T
N A V A L A C A D E M Y N O T N E R T G O
P R I N C E T O N S L L A F A R A G A I N
D E L M A R D N A L S I G N O L V A P E N
```

21. Delaware

1. LIBERTY AND INDEPENDENCE (**D**)
2. BLUE HEN CHICKEN (**E**)
3. WILMINGTON (**L**)
4. AMERICAN HOLLY (**A**)
5. SMALL WONDER (**W**)
6. FIRST STATE (**A**)
7. POULTRY (**R**)
8. DOVER (**E**)

22. Maryland

1 THURGOOD**M**ARSHALL
2 ANN**A**POLIS
3 BABE**R**UTH
4 BLACKE**Y**EDSUSAN
5 BA**L**TIMORE
6 THESTARSP**A**NGLEDBANNER
7 UPTONSI**N**CLAIR
8 FREDERICK**D**OUGLASS

23. New Jersey

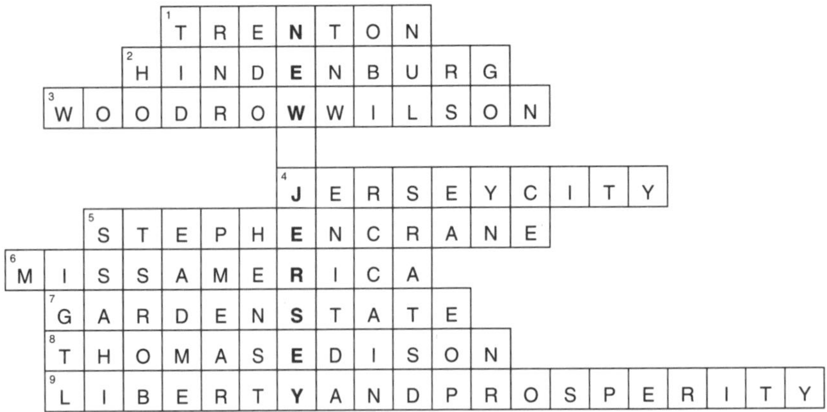

24. New York

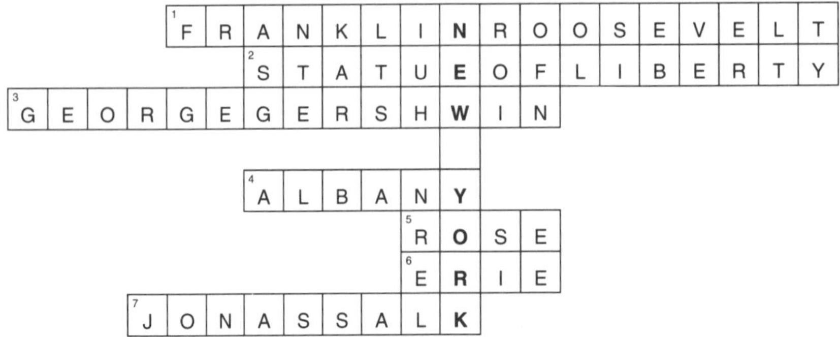

25. Pennsylvania

1. PHILADEL**P**HIA
2. ST**E**EL
3. MARIANA**N**DERSON
4. STEPHE**N**FOSTER
5. HARRI**S**BURG
6. KE**Y**STONESTATE
7. HEM**L**OCK
8. **V**ALLEYFORGE
9. ANDREWC**A**RNEGIE
10. BENJAMI**N**FRANKLIN
11. MOUNTA**I**NLAUREL
12. QU**A**KERSTATE

26. West Virginia

1. STONE**W**ALLJACKSON
2. CHARL**E**STON
3. PEARL**S**BUCK
4. MOUN**T**AINSTATE
5. NEWRI**V**ERGORGE
6. CARD**I**NAL
7. HARPE**R**SFERRY
8. HUNTIN**G**TON
9. COALM**I**NING
10. RHODODE**N**DRON
11. MARTINROB**I**NSONDELANY
12. KAN**A**WHA

27. The Southern States—I

1 FLORIDA
2 KENTUCKY
3 NORTHCAROLINA; NORTH
4 KENTUCKY
5 KENTUCKY
6 VIRGINIA
7 ARKANSAS
8 MISSISSIPPI
9 KENTUCKY
10 GEORGIA
11 TENNESSEE
12 KENTUCKY
13 TENNESSEE
14 KENTUCKY
15 NORTHCAROLINA
16 GEORGIA
17 TENNESSEE
18 TENNESSEE
19 MISSISSIPPI
20 TENNESSEE
21 VIRGINIA
22 VIRGINIA
23 ARKANSAS
24 TEXAS
25 ALABAMA
26 ALABAMA
27 SOUTHCAROLINA
28 VIRGINIA
29 GEORGIA
30 TENNESSEE
31 NORTHCAROLINA
32 VIRGINIA
33 ALABAMA
34 LOUISIANA
35 LOUISIANA
36 OKLAHOMA
37 VIRGINIA
38 ALABAMA
39 GEORGIA
40 SOUTHCAROLINA
41 OKLAHOMA
42 ARKANSAS
43 FLORIDA; FLORIDA
44 NORTHCAROLINA
45 TEXAS
46 TEXAS
47 SOUTH
48 VIRGINIA
49 FLORIDA
50 SOUTH
51 OKLAHOMA

28. The Southern States—II

1	MARGARE**T**MITCHELL
2	JIMT**H**ORPE
3	SOON**E**RSTATE
4	RO**S**APARKS
5	JEFFERS**O**NDAVIS
6	MO**U**NTMITCHELL
7	CAPEHA**T**TERAS
8	ALT**H**EAGIBSON
9	JACKI**E**ROBINSON
10	ZACHA**R**YTAYLOR
11	ARLI**N**GTON
12	JAME**S**KPOLK
13	MON**T**ICELLO
14	ABRAH**A**MLINCOLN
15	MOUN**T**VERNON
16	VOLUNT**E**ERSTATE
17	PARRI**S**ISLAND

29. The Southern States—III

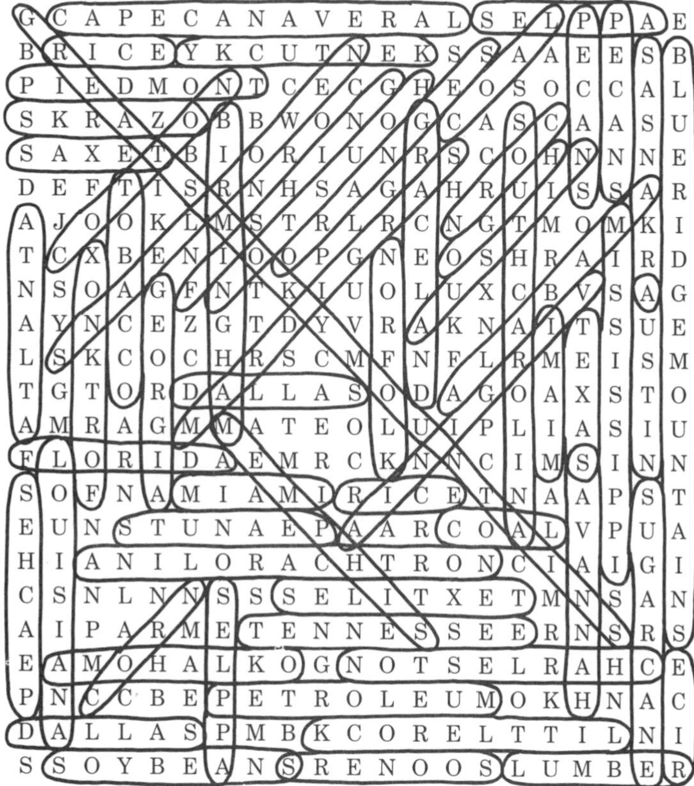

30. Alabama

1 ROS**A**PARKS
2 SE**L**MA
3 WCH**A**NDY
4 MO**B**ILE
5 GEORGEW**A**LLACE
6 BIR**M**INGHAM
7 YELLOWH**A**MMER

31. Arkansas

1 HATTIEC**A**RAWAY
2 **R**ICE
3 MOC**K**INGBIRD
4 DIZZYDE**A**N
5 PI**N**E
6 DOUGLA**S**MACARTHUR
7 OZ**A**RKS
8 HOT**S**PRINGS

32. Florida

1 OKE**F**ENOKEE
2 EVERG**L**ADES
3 OSCE**O**LA
4 INGODWET**R**UST
5 SEM**I**NOLE
6 MARYMCLEO**D**BETHUNE
7 CAPEC**A**NAVERAL

33. Georgia

1 MARGARETMITCHELL
2 MARTINLUTHERKINGJR
3 TRAILOFTEARS
4 JACKIEROBINSON
5 CALLAWAYGARDENS
6 ELIWHITNEY
7 VIDALIA

34. Kentucky

1 FORTKNOX
2 BLUEGRASSSTATE
3 GOLDENROD
4 TOBACCOSTATE
5 LOUISVILLE
6 LINCOLN
7 KENTUCKYDERBY
8 ZACHARYTAYLOR

35. Louisiana

1 NEWORLEANS
2 BATONROUGE
3 EDWARDDOUGLASSWHITE
4 PELICANSTATE
5 LOUISARMSTRONG
6 MARDIGRAS
7 JEANLAFITTE
8 TRUMANCAPOTE
9 JAZZ

36. Mississippi

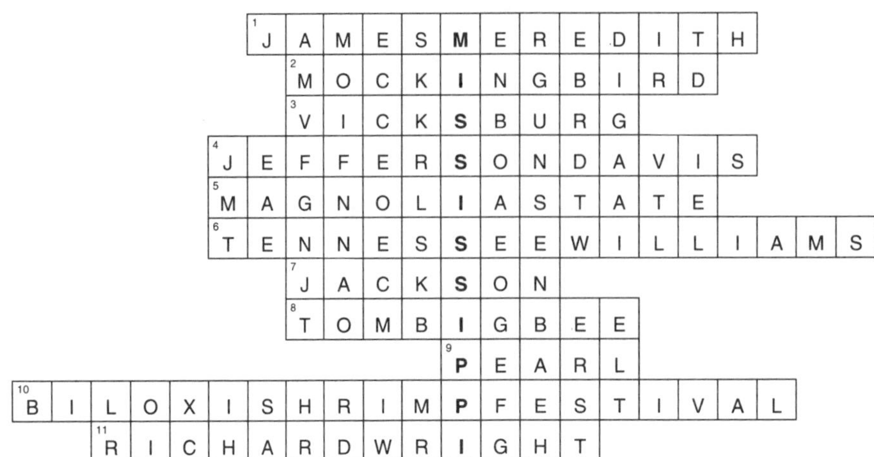

37. North Carolina

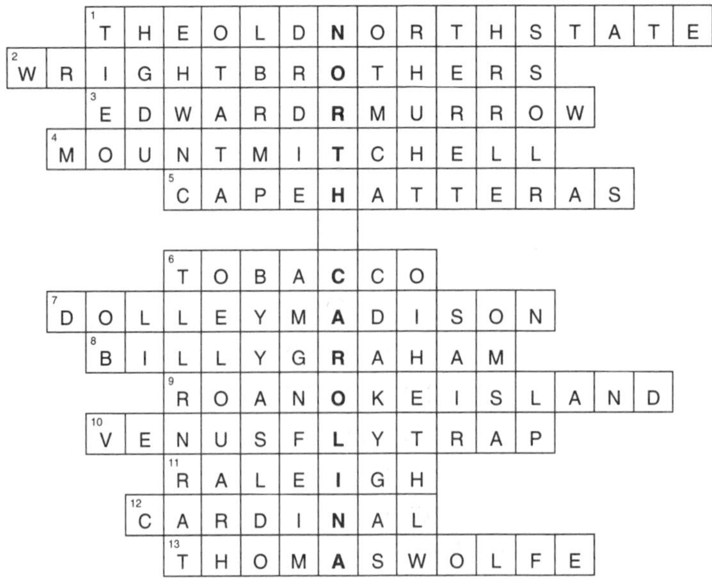

38. Oklahoma

1 SOONERSTATE
2 ARKANSAS
3 MISTLETOE
4 CIMARRON
5 JIMTHORPE
6 OKLAHOMACITY
7 MICKEYMANTLE
8 CANADIAN

39. South Carolina

1. PARRISISLAND
2. COOPER
3. FORTSUMTER
4. PALMETTO
5. HUGO
6. RICE
7. JOHNCCALHOUN
8. MARION
9. YELLOWJESSAMINE
10. COLUMBIA
11. CAROLINAWREN
12. SANTEE
13. ALTHEAGIBSON

40. Tennessee

1. VOLUNTEERSTATE
2. GRACELAND
3. MOCKINGBIRD
4. ALVINYORK
5. GRANDOLEOPRY
6. JAMESKPOLK
7. NASHVILLE
8. MEMPHIS
9. CUMBERLAND

41. Texas

1. AUSTIN
2. BLUEBONNET
3. MEXICO
4. DALLAS
5. SAMHOUSTON

42. Virginia

			1 M	O	U	N	T	**V**	E	R	N	O	N		
				2 M	O	N	T	**I**	C	E	L	L	O		
				3 R	O	B	E	**R**	T	E	L	E	E		
4 F	L	O	W	E	R	I	N	**G**	D	O	G	W	O	O	D
				5 C	A	R	D	**I**	N	A	L				
				6 A	R	L	I	**N**	G	T	O	N			
		7 O	L	D	D	O	M	**I**	N	I	O	N			
			8 E	D	G	A	R	**A**	L	L	A	N	P	O	E

43. The Midwestern States—I

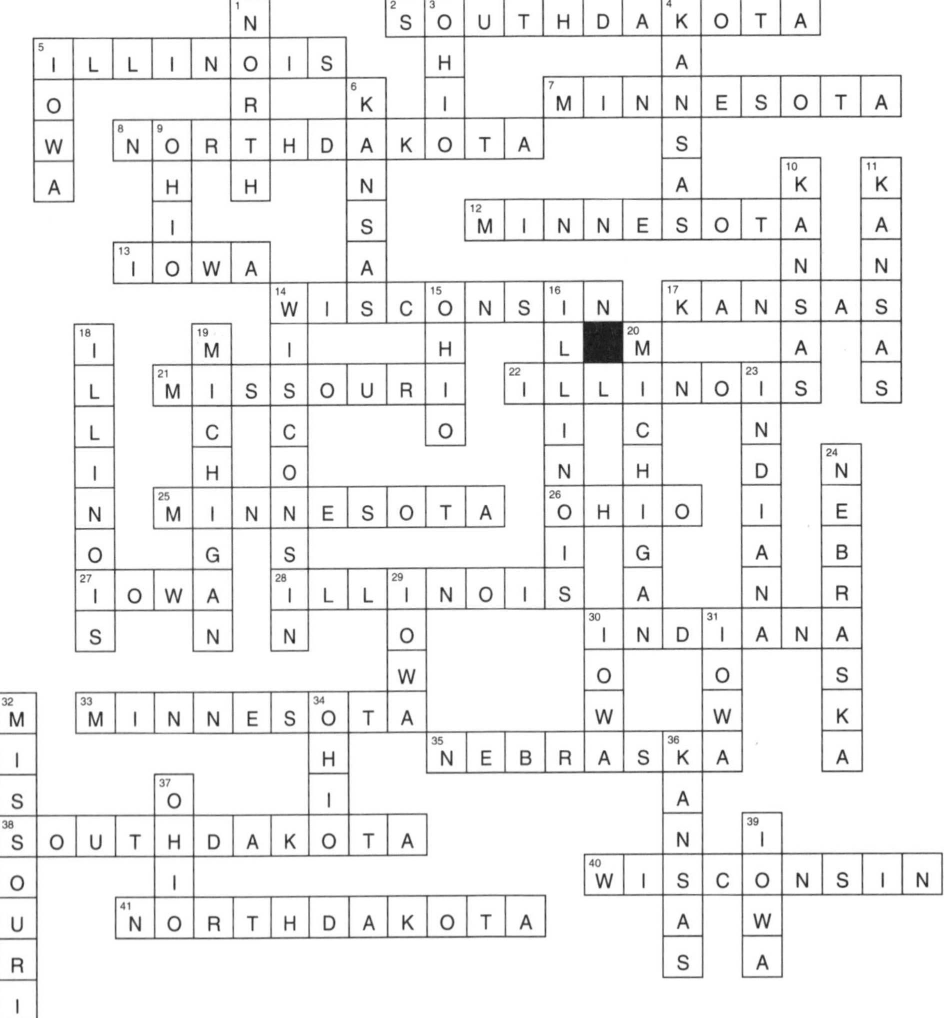

44. The Midwestern States—II

1. DE**T**ROIT
2. BLACK**H**ILLS
3. HOOSI**E**RSTATE
4. KALA**M**AZOO
5. DWIGHTE**I**SENHOWER
6. RONAL**D**REAGAN
7. HA**W**KEYESTATE
8. BATTL**E**CREEK
9. MOUNTRU**S**HMORE
10. HARRY**T**RUMAN
11. WOLV**E**RINESTATE
12. GOPHE**R**STATE
13. CYCLO**N**ESTATE
14. AMERICA**S**DAIRYLAND
15. HERBER**T**HOOVER
16. M**A**YOCLINIC
17. SEARS**T**OWER
18. AMELIA**E**ARHART
19. CORNHU**S**KERSTATE

45. The Midwestern States—III

```
B S A F D A I R Y I N G A O O G A C I H C
G R E A T L A K E S K B K I O W A N N E I
A T O K A D H T U O S L O H M H D K D T N
R A S D N A T I H C I W I O A I J Y I T C
Y I I N C A F O G M R H H M A H T K A A I
C R O A T O K A D H T R O N S I W M N L N
S O N L S L R E R G B L A I C K I C A P N
C E I E I Y A N P G A P M S A S S O S H A
C P L V B N N O C O O A A N H W C R A A T
N M L E E R C T C L T S S O H I O N M S I
L I I L O E A O I C N A H S B S N I P T P
O N G C V E K S L A S I A U U A S R O P A
C N N B H N C U K N O B T B K S I S M A I
N E I W M I L K A A A T M S O N N K A U P
I S S F A R G O W W E U A U G Y S C H L I
L O N O S I D A M R L R R F D C S O A M E
F T A F A F G O N O B I I M U T C T I W R
O A L E S E E H C E S E M J L V T S O A R
D E T R O I T I N K L I M O U E B E W W E
N G A B A D L A N D S B U T T E R V A O N
A H A M O G A B E N N I W C H G N I B I J
L C F E S K C R A M S I B B R T O L E D O
```

46. Illinois

1 E R N E S T H E M **I** N G W A Y

2 R O N A **L** D R E A G A N

3 L A N D O F **L** I N C O L N

4 W A L T D **I** S N E Y

5 S P R I **N** G F I E L D

6 L I N C **O** L N

7 C H **I** C A G O

8 S E A R **S** T O W E R

47. Indiana

1 G U S G R **I** S S O M
2 P E O **N** Y
3 C A R **D** I N A L
4 T U L **I** P P O P L A R
5 H O O S I E R S T **A** T E
6 I N D I A **N** A P O L I S
7 W A B **A** S H

48. Iowa

1 B U F F A L O B **I** L L C O D Y
2 H E R B E R T H **O** O V E R
3 J O H N **W** A Y N E
4 H **A** W K E Y E S T A T E

49. Kansas

1 T O P E **K** A
2 A M E L I A E **A** R H A R T
3 C A R R Y **N** A T I O N
4 D W I G H T E I **S** E N H O W E R
5 H O M E O N T H E R **A** N G E
6 A R K A N **S** A S

50. Michigan

1. KALA**M**AZOO
2. DETRO**I**T
3. BATTLE**C**REEK
4. JOHN**H**KELLOGG
5. WOLVER**I**NESTATE
6. LANSIN**G**
7. AMERIC**A**NROBIN
8. HE**N**RYFORD

51. Minnesota

1. COM**M**ONLOON
2. FSCOTTF**I**TZGERALD
3. CHARLESLI**N**DBERGH
4. PAULBU**N**YAN
5. WARREN**E**BURGER
6. LADYS**S**LIPPER
7. MAY**O**CLINIC
8. LAKEI**T**ASCA
9. SINCL**A**IRLEWIS

52. Missouri

1. HARRYTRU**M**AN
2. JOSEPH**I**NEBAKER
3. DRED**S**COTT
4. JES**S**EJAMES
5. STL**O**UIS
6. JOSEPHP**U**LITZER
7. JOHNJPE**R**SHING
8. GEORGEWASH**I**NGTONCARVER

53. Nebraska

1. LINCOLN
2. GOLDENROD
3. EQUALITYBEFORETHELAW
4. NIOBRARA
5. PLATTE
6. BOYSTOWN
7. CORNHUSKERSTATE
8. OMAHA

54. North Dakota

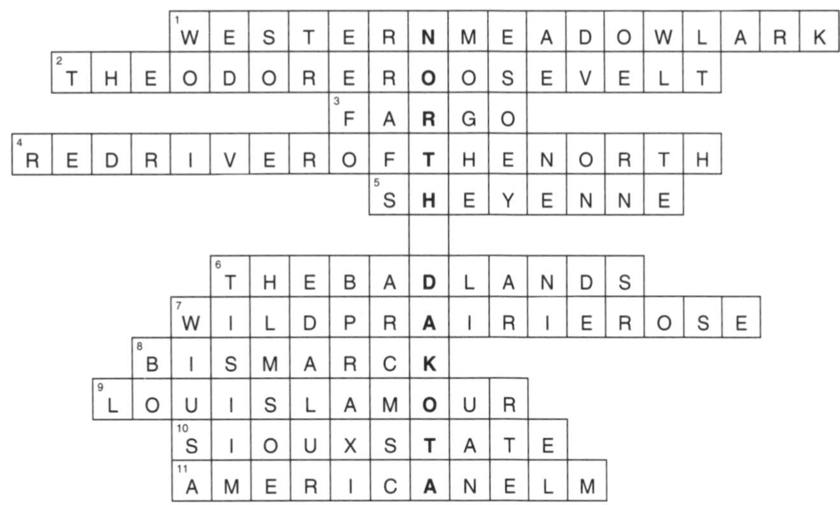

55. Ohio

1. OBERLIN
2. AMISH
3. CARDINAL
4. COLUMBUS

56. South Dakota

1. MIS**S**OURI
2. SI**O**UXFALLS
3. SITTINGB**U**LL
4. BIGS**T**ONE
5. CRAZY**H**ORSE
6. WOUN**D**EDKNEE
7. O**A**HE
8. BLAC**K**HILLS
9. GUTZONB**O**RGLUM
10. UNDERGOD**T**HEPEOPLERULE
11. J**A**MES

57. Wisconsin

1. MIL**W**AUKEE
2. WOODV**I**OLET
3. **S**TCROIX
4. SPEN**C**ERTRACY
5. FRANKLL**O**YDWRIGHT
6. AMERICA**N**ROBIN
7. AMERICA**S**DAIRYLAND
8. MAD**I**SON
9. WIN**N**EBAGO

58. The Rocky Mountain States—I

Across:
1. WYOMING
5. WYOMING
11. NEVADA
13. MONTANA
15. COLORADO
16. ARIZONA
18. WYOMING
20. COLORADO
24. NEVADA
25. ARIZONA
26. COLORADO
27. NEVADA
28. NEVADA
29. UTAH

Down:
2. NEWMEXICO
3. MONTANA
4. COLORADO
6. IDAHO
7. IDAHO
8. MONTANA
9. NEWMEXICO
10. UTAH
12. ARIZONA
14. ARIZONA
17. COLORADO
19. NEVADA
21. ARIZONA
22. IDAHO
23. IDAHO
24. NEVADA

59. The Rocky Mountain States—II

1. OLDFAI**T**HFUL
2. BEE**H**IVESTATE
3. LASV**E**GAS
4. JIMB**R**IDGER
5. SANDRA**O**CONNOR
6. GRAND**C**ANYON
7. GEORGIAO**K**EEFFE
8. BIGSK**Y**COUNTRY
9. GE**M**STATE
10. COLORAD**O**SPRINGS
11. EQ**U**ALITYSTATE
12. WYOMI**N**G
13. LAKE**T**AHOE
14. BRIGH**A**MYOUNG
15. CENTENN**I**ALSTATE
16. LANDOFE**N**CHANTMENT
17. YELLOW**S**TONE
18. SILVERS**T**ATE
19. KITC**A**RSON
20. GRAND**T**ETONS
21. N**E**VADA
22. PIKE**S**PEAK

60. The Rocky Mountain States—III

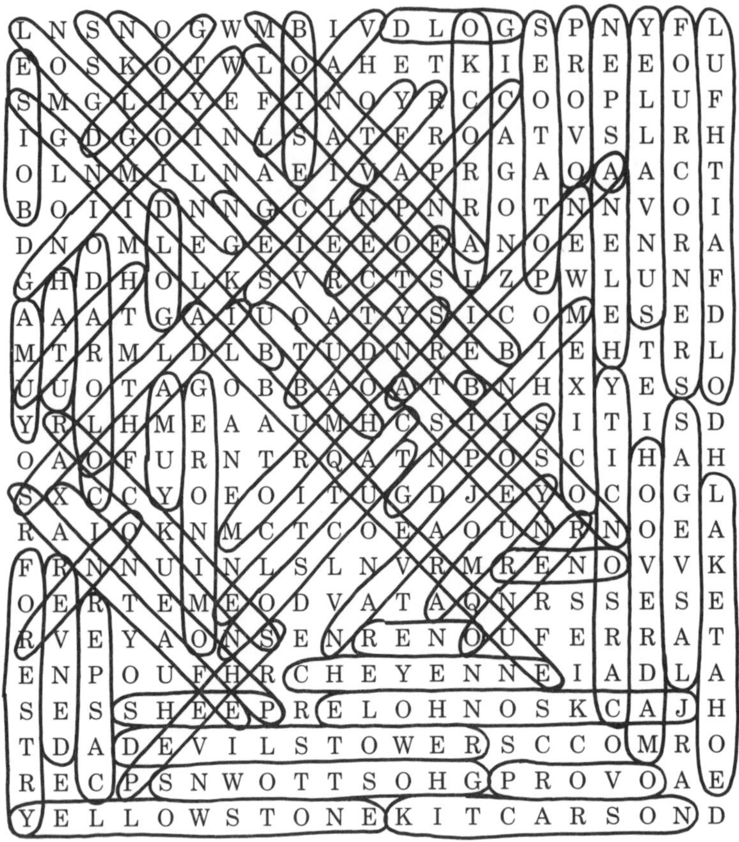

61. Arizona

1 G	R	A	N	D	C	**A**	N	Y	O	N	
			2 O	K	C	O	**R**	R	A	L	
	3 G	E	R	O	N	**I**	M	O			
						4 **Z**	U	N	I		
				5 A	J	**O**					
			6 P	H	O	E	**N**	I	X		
				7 O	R	**A**	I	B	I		

62. Colorado

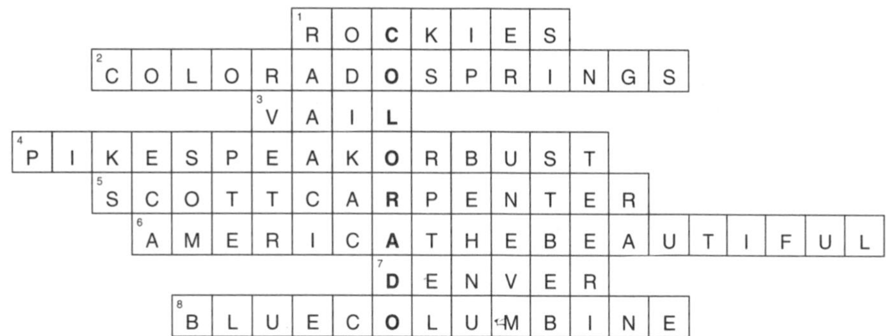

63. Idaho

1 BO**I**SE
2 BAL**D**
3 POT**A**TOES
4 WESTERNW**H**ITEPINE
5 ARC**O**

64. Montana

1 WESTERN**M**EADOWLARK
2 BITTERR**O**OT
3 HELE**N**A
4 JEANNET**T**ERANKIN
5 MOUNT**A**INSTATE
6 BILLI**N**GS
7 CL**A**RKFORK

65. Nevada

1 C A R S O N C I T Y
2 L A S V E G A S
3 L A S V E G A S
4 L A K E T A H O E
5 B O U L D E R D A M
6 S I L V E R S T A T E

66. New Mexico

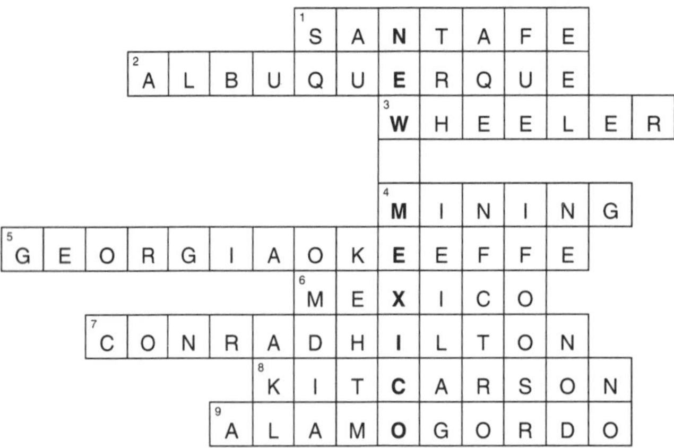

67. Utah

1 S E A G U L L
2 I N D U S T R Y
3 S A L T L A K E C I T Y
4 B E E H I V E S T A T E

68. Wyoming

1. YELLO**W**STONE
2. NELLIETA**Y**LOEROSS
3. COTT**O**NWOOD
4. JI**M**BRIDGER
5. OLDFA**I**THFUL
6. CHEYE**N**NE
7. EQUALRI**G**HTS

69. The Pacific Coast States—I

1. CRA**T**ERLAKE
2. MOUNTW**H**ITNEY
3. EVERGR**E**ENSTATE
4. SAN**P**EDRO
5. RICH**A**RDNIXON
6. CAS**C**ADES
7. SAND**I**EGO
8. CALI**F**ORNIA
9. JOHNSTE**I**NBECK
10. GRAND**C**OULEE
11. BING**C**ROSBY
12. AST**O**RIA
13. NAP**A**VALLEY
14. GEORGE**S**PATTON
15. SUNSE**T**STATE
16. DI**S**NEYLAND
17. JAMESWHI**T**TAKER
18. LOS**A**NGELES
19. MOUNTS**T**HELENS
20. SPAC**E**NEEDLE
21. GOLDEN**S**TATE

70. The Pacific Coast States—II

```
O F E U G E N E C S O S A L E M E C C E T
C U T O R E G O N A A R S H C D O O O S A
S P A L M S P R I N G S S S O N H T L O C
I R G E A P N P D A D I I O D R A W U J O
C S N E E N M I R N F E H O E G T Y M N M
N M E R T Y E E S D R T R B R O F Y B A A
A A D Y L G D A E R M A M A E L K R I S E
R D L O O W I L A E R I P U L D A S A R N
F A O A O O I N G A T E R A O I L O E O R
N T G O U O E L S S S E V U D A O S M E R
A M D Q W V F E L F K N O L P R N L I A D
S S E E A Y A F R A I A O P I O A N T N E
H S E D R T L U E U M G L S E S I C U A A
P H A B T M S L Q L O E E L R A H O O H T
O S U L E G T A O T S G T T R S S N N E H
R I E L I T O H H H W T T T I T O D O I V
T F A B A J I L N S A H M F E M T O G M A
L S H C N I L S D C T C A G O V E R E N L
A Q U A C U L T U R E M U L T I A S R N L
N M S I R U O T E N A P P L E S T L O A E
D N E W N F O R T Y N I N E R S A T L Y Y
S P O K A N E T R E S E D E V A J O M E I
S I E R R A C L U B O T N E M A R C A S Y
```

71. California

1. SANFRAN**C**ISCO
2. CAL**A**VERAS
3. GO**L**DENSTATE
4. FORTYN**I**NERS
5. DWGRI**F**FITH
6. C**O**NDOR
7. EU**R**EKA
8. JOH**N**MUIR
9. MTWH**I**TNEY
10. MOJ**A**VE

72. Oregon

1. OREG**O**NGRAPE
2. PO**R**TLAND
3. CRAT**E**RLAKE
4. DOU**G**LASFIR
5. R**O**GUE
6. SU**N**SETSTATE

73. Washington

1. JAMES**W**HITTAKER
2. SN**A**KE
3. CA**S**CADES
4. MTST**H**ELENS
5. YAK**I**MA
6. SPACE**N**EEDLE
7. EVER**G**REENSTATE
8. SEA**T**TLE
9. BINGCR**O**SBY
10. GRA**N**DCOULEE

74. Alaska—I

1. PETROLEUM
2. PERMAFROST
3. REINDEER
4. PRUDHOE BAY
5. YUKON
6. FISHING
7. LAST FRONTIER
8. NORTH TO THE FUTURE
9. PRINCE WILLIAM
10. MOUNT MCKINLEY
11. ESKIMOS
12. VALDEZ
13. JUNEAU
14. KENAI FJORDS
15. BERING STRAIT
16. ANCHORAGE
17. IDITAROD
18. WILLIAM H SEWARD
19. ALEUTIAN
20. FAIRBANKS

Down (bold letters): LAND OF THE MIDNIGHT SUN

75. Alaska—II

76. Hawaii—I

1. PINEA**P**PLES
2. MOUNTW**A**IALEALE
3. TOU**R**ISM
4. PEARLH**A**RBOR
5. DIAMON**D**HEAD
6. HIB**I**SCUS
7. POLYNE**S**IA
8. JAM**E**SCOOK
9. HON**O**LULU
10. COF**F**EEBEANS
11. A**T**OLLS
12. OA**H**U
13. KALA**E**
14. **P**OI
15. MAUN**A**LOA
16. SUGAR**C**ANE
17. LIL**I**UOKALANI
18. SUR**F**ING
19. USSAR**I**ZONA
20. SANDWI**C**HISLANDS

77. Hawaii—II

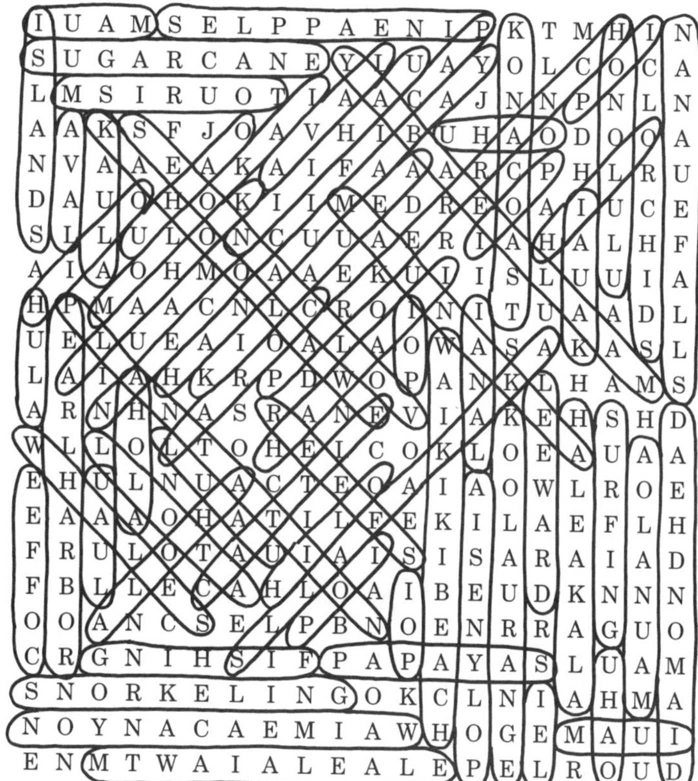

78. Our Nation's Capital

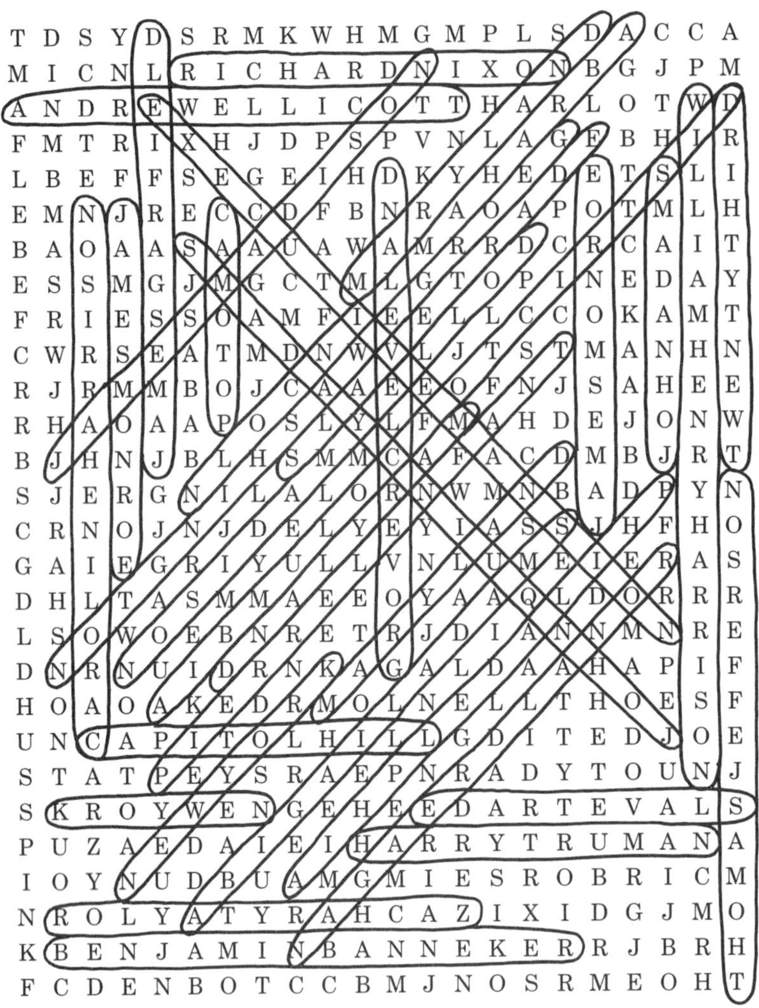

1. Benjamin Banneker
2. Maryland
3. James Madison
4. Harry Truman
5. Executive Mansion
6. Grover Cleveland
7. Potomac
8. William Henry Harrison
9. New York
10. Dolley Madison
11. Zachary Taylor
12. England
13. Richard Nixon
14. District of Columbia
15. Pierre L'Enfant
16. Twenty-third
17. John Quincy Adams
18. Capitol Hill
19. George Washington
20. James Monroe
21. slave trade
22. Caroline Harrison
23. Philadelphia
24. Thomas Jefferson
25. Ronald Reagan
26. John Adams
27. Abraham Lincoln
28. Andrew Ellicott
29. James Garfield
30. Abigail Adams

79. Famous Cities in the United States—I

1 STLOUIS
1 SANTAFE
2 ARCO
3 ATLANTA
4 DETROIT
5 NEWPORT
6 OMAHA
7 MONTPELIER
8 MORRISTOWN
9 AJO
10 STAUGUSTINE
11 NEWBRUNSWICK
12 SELMA
13 MONTGOMERY
14 RICHMOND
15 TOMBSTONE
16 HOBOKEN
17 ANCHORAGE
18 HOLLYWOOD
19 BIRMINGHAM
20 NOME
21 BOSTON
22 LITTLEROCK
23 ATLANTICCITY
24 ANNAPOLIS
25 TUSKEGEE
26 ABILENE
27 PARIS
28 COOPERSTOWN
29 NASHVILLE
30 VICKSBURG
31 VIDALIA
32 HARTFORD
33 MEMPHIS
34 PITTSBURGH
35 DALLAS
36 HANNIBAL
37 BUFFALO
38 BRUNSWICK
39 LAKEHURST
40 KEYWEST
41 LASVEGAS

80. Famous Cities in the United States—II

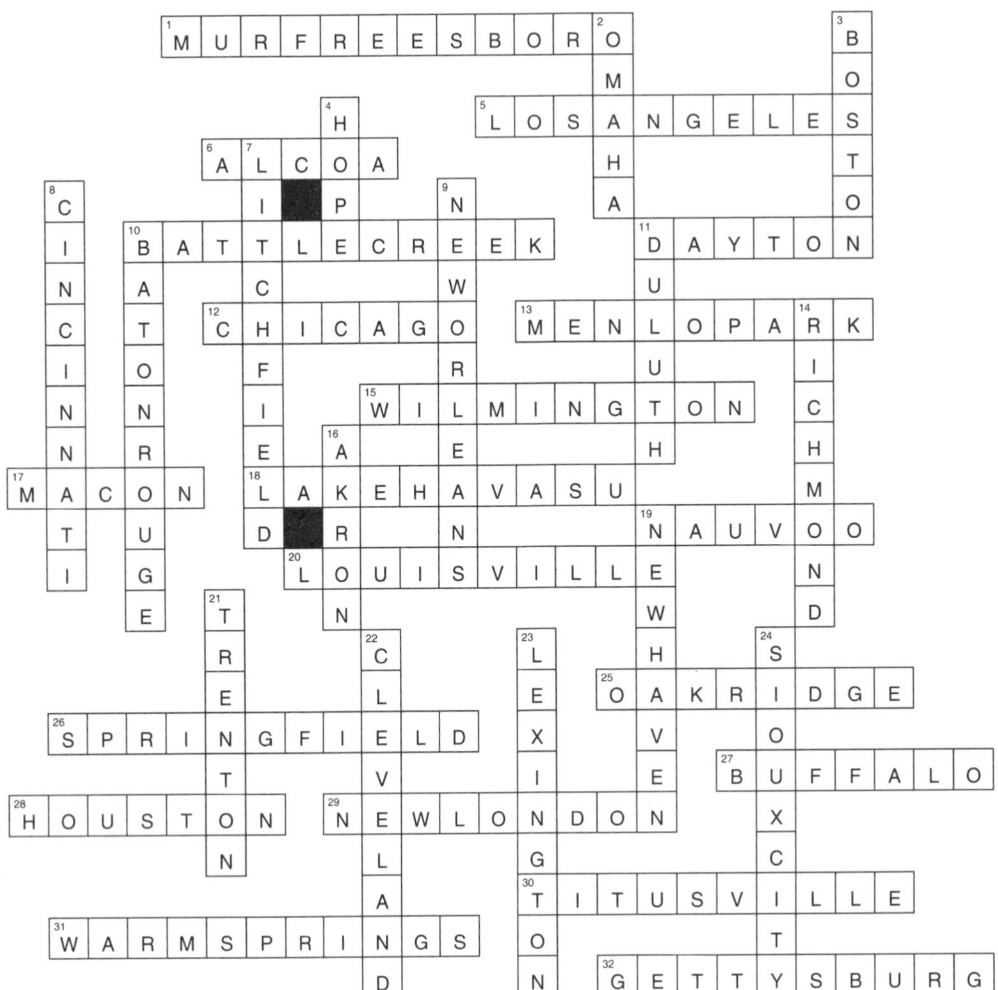

81. Rivers of the United States—I

1. FLO**R**IDA
2. WASH**I**NGTON
3. PENNSYL**V**ANIA
4. OR**E**GON
5. NEWJE**R**SEY
6. RHODEI**S**LAND
7. GE**O**RGIA
8. CALI**F**ORNIA
9. KEN**T**UCKY
10. NEW**H**AMPSHIRE
11. NEWM**E**XICO
12. MASSACH**U**SETTS
13. MO**N**TANA
14. MICH**I**GAN
15. CONNEC**T**ICUT
16. TENN**E**SSEE
17. NORTH**D**AKOTA
18. MIS**S**OURI
19. U**T**AH
20. ARK**A**NSAS
21. **T**EXAS
22. MAIN**E**
23. MINNE**S**OTA

82. Rivers of the United States—II

1. MA**R**YLAND
2. IND**I**ANA
3. NE**V**ADA
4. V**E**RMONT
5. NEB**R**ASKA
6. LOUI**S**IANA

7. ARIZ**O**NA
8. CALI**F**ORNIA

9. WES**T**VIRGINIA
10. OKLA**H**OMA
11. N**E**WYORK

12. SO**U**THDAKOTA
13. KA**N**SAS
14. VIRG**I**NIA
15. NOR**T**HCAROLINA
16. D**E**LAWARE
17. I**D**AHO

18. ALA**S**KA
19. **T**EXAS
20. SOUTHC**A**ROLINA
21. U**T**AH
22. NEWJ**E**RSEY
23. WISCON**S**IN

83. Lakes and Bodies of Water in the United States

1. WINNEBAGO
2. REELFOOT
3. ERIE
4. MAALAEA
5. TAMPA / TEXOMA
6. CHAMPLAIN
7. ONTARIO
8. CHESAPEAKE
9. SARATOGA SPRINGS
10. BARNEGAT
11. TAHOE
12. CAPE COD
13. ATCHAFALAYA
14. MEAD / MOBILE
15. OKEECHOBEE
16. KEYSTONE
17. HOT SPRINGS
18. SAGINAW
19. GREAT SALT
20. WINNIPESAUKEE
21. ERIE
22. BIG STONE
23. MOOSEHEAD
24. CRATER
25. NORRIS
26. HAVASU
27. HURON
28. PUGET / PLACID
29. NANTUCKET
30. OAHE
31. GREEN
32. POWELL
33. PAMLICO
34. WALDEN
35. FLATHEAD
36. TAHOE
37. MICHIGAN
38. SUPERIOR
39. PRUDHOE

84. Mountains and Rivers of the United States

Across

2 JEMEZ
6 COLUMBIA
7 WHITE
9 BRAZOS
13 RUBY
15 THAMES
18 CATSKILL
20 PLATTE
23 MIAMI
24 ALLEGHENY
25 YAZOO
28 WICHITA
31 SUSQUEHANNA
32 MONONGAHELA
34 NEUSE
38 PEARL
39 VIRGIN
40 PINE
41 PEACE
43 RED
44 ROANOKE
47 OSAGE
50 SNAKE
51 YUKON
53 SNAKE
54 CHARLES
55 KALAMAZOO
57 APPALACHIAN
59 BIGHORN
61 PINE
62 CONNECTICUT
63 BITTERROOT
64 COLORADO

Down

1 YORK
2 JAMES
3 ELK
4 OHIO
5 ROGUE
8 TRUCKEE
9 BLACKHILLS
10 WHITE
11 CASCADE
12 SMOKY
14 YELLOWSTONE
16 BLUERIDGE
17 SHEYENNE
19 ADIRONDACK
21 SACRAMENTO
22 OZARK
26 MISSOURI
27 DELAWARE
29 HUDSON
30 ARKANSAS
33 SAVANNAH
35 GREEN
36 CHIPPEWA
37 JAMES
38 PECOS
42 SALMON
44 RIOGRANDE
45 MISSOURI
46 WABASH
48 PAWTUXET
49 PEEDEE
52 GRAND
56 MOBILE
58 PECOS
60 GILA

85. High Points of the United States

		1 G																		
	2 N	E	V	3 A	D	A				4 O	K	L	A	H	O	5 M	A			
		O		L												A				
		R		6 A	R	I	Z	7 O	N	8 A				9 T		S		10 M		11 I
		G		B				R		12 R	H	O	D	E	I	S	L	A	N	D
		13 I	D	A	H	14 O		E		K				N		A		R		A
		A	■	M	■	H		G		A		15 W		N		C		Y		H
			16 C	A	L	I	F	O	R	N	I	A		E		H		L		O
			O			O		N		S		S		S		17 U	T	A	H	
			N							A		H		S		S		N		
	18 C		19 N	E	W	20 H	A	M	P	S	H	I	R	E		E		D		21 I
	O		E			A						N		E		T				L
	L		C			22 W	Y	O	M	I	N	G				T				L
23 M	O	N	T	A	N	A						24 T	E	X	25 A	S				I
	R		I			I		26 O				O			L					N
	A		C		27 M	I	C	H	I	G	A	N		28 M	A	I	N	E		O
	D		U					I							S					I
29 N	O	R	T	H	C	A	R	O	L	I	N	A			30 K	A	N	S	A	S
															A					

86. Islands in the United States

```
A E U G A E T O C N I H C T M L C R K M
E H I L T O N H E A D S I R R A P J A A
N K E Y W E S T P M D L M O L O K A I C
A E U G A E T A S S A D A A A B J E D K
T B O S S A R T E K C U T N A N F K O I
T A G E H R L I E R I F I O A I O N K N
A M R N I Y J E K Y L L M K R I E O A A
H U A S N R B U U P A D R E L K H R E C
N M L R G Y H K A T M T D E S E R T T G
A P Y G T A A S A N I B E L N Y R H T D
M G E O O H V C R H W A S S A W E M O A
A G K A N S A E G N O L N E C E N A L Q
R P J O U T V S R N B O D I E S Y N R U
I R E S N L I H V Y M A L N P T A I A I
W U E A I A T B O I S B L A N C C T H D
E D S V V W P T S U N K I E W W S O C N
S E L E A R A Y M A D E L I N E I U N E
O N A R K E C B P M N L Y I P A B L E C
T C N Y L N B E L N I I H A U I Y U E K
M E A L A C A E A S M S D A R J E H U R
U B I O B E D H Y C H R K W T D K A Q O
A S Y S A N C L E M E N T E L T S O P A
```

Manhattan	New York	Maui	Hawaii
St. Lawrence	Alaska	Kodiak	Alaska
Key West	Florida	Pecan	Louisiana
Jekyll	Georgia	Santa Catalina	California
Avery	Louisiana	Martha's Vineyard	Massachusetts
Assateague	Maryland	Hilton Head	South Carolina
Madeline	Wisconsin	Simons	Georgia
Molokai	Hawaii	Chincoteague	Virginia
Prudence	Rhode Island	Aquidneck	Rhode Island
Padre	Texas	Kauai	Hawaii
Captiva	Florida	Key Largo	Florida
Channel	California	Apostle	Wisconsin
Mackinac	Michigan	Long	New York
Queen Charlotte	Alaska	Tybee	Georgia
Mt. Desert	Maine	Pea	North Carolina
Lanai	Hawaii	Aleutian	Alaska
Bois Blanc	Michigan	Washington	Wisconsin
Wassaw	Georgia	Kahoolawe	Hawaii
Nunivak	Alaska	Sanibel	Florida
Fire	New York	Beaver	Michigan
Nantucket	Massachusetts	North Manitou	Michigan
Key Biscayne	Florida	San Clemente	California
Parris	South Carolina	Niihau	Hawaii
Roanoke	North Carolina	Bodie	North Carolina
Oahu	Hawaii	Ellis	New York

87. State Name Origins

1 COLORADO
2 OHIO
3 MISSISSIPPI
4 IOWA
5 FLORIDA
6 MONTANA
7 TEXAS
8 MISSOURI
9 IDAHO
10 ALABAMA
11 NEBRASKA
12 NEVADA
12 NEWYORK
13 LOUISIANA
14 WASHINGTON
15 GEORGIA
16 WISCONSIN
17 NORTHCAROLINA
17 NEWHAMPSHIRE
18 TENNESSEE
19 ARKANSAS
20 ARIZONA
21 MAINE
22 KENTUCKY
23 IOWA
24 MASSACHUSETTS
25 ALASKA
26 SOUTHCAROLINA
27 VERMONT
28 KANSAS
29 RHODEISLAND
30 VIRGINIA
31 UTAH
32 CONNECTICUT
33 HAWAII
34 INDIANA
35 PENNSYLVANIA
36 OREGON
37 SOUTHDAKOTA
38 ILLINOIS
39 CALIFORNIA
40 IDAHO
41 OHIO
42 IOWA
43 IDAHO
44 MARYLAND
45 OKLAHOMA
46 OREGON
47 NEWMEXICO

88. State Nicknames—I

1 MAINE
2 NEW YORK / NEVADA
3 PENNSYLVANIA
4 MISSOURI
5 NEBRASKA
6 COLORADO
7 TENNESSEE
8 MAINE
9 VERMONT
10 NEBRASKA
11 VIRGINIA
12 ILLINOIS / INDIANA
13 ARIZONA
14 FLORIDA
15 ILLINOIS
16 ALASKA
17 IDAHO
18 HAWAII
19 NEW MEXICO
20 NEW HAMPSHIRE
21 WYOMING
22 NEVADA
23 CALIFORNIA
24 OHIO
25 ALASKA
26 MAINE
27 WISCONSIN
28 OHIO / OHIO
29 HAWAII
30 ILLINOIS
31 LOUISIANA
32 KANSAS
33 MISSOURI
34 COLORADO
35 OKLAHOMA
36 UTAH
37 MICHIGAN
38 VIRGINIA
39 MONTANA
40 MISSISSIPPI
41 LOUISIANA
42 OREGON
43 IDAHO
44 ALASKA
45 WASHINGTON
46 IOWA
47 IOWA
48 OREGON
49 HAWAII
50 UTAH
51 MAINE
52 UTAH

89. State Nicknames—II

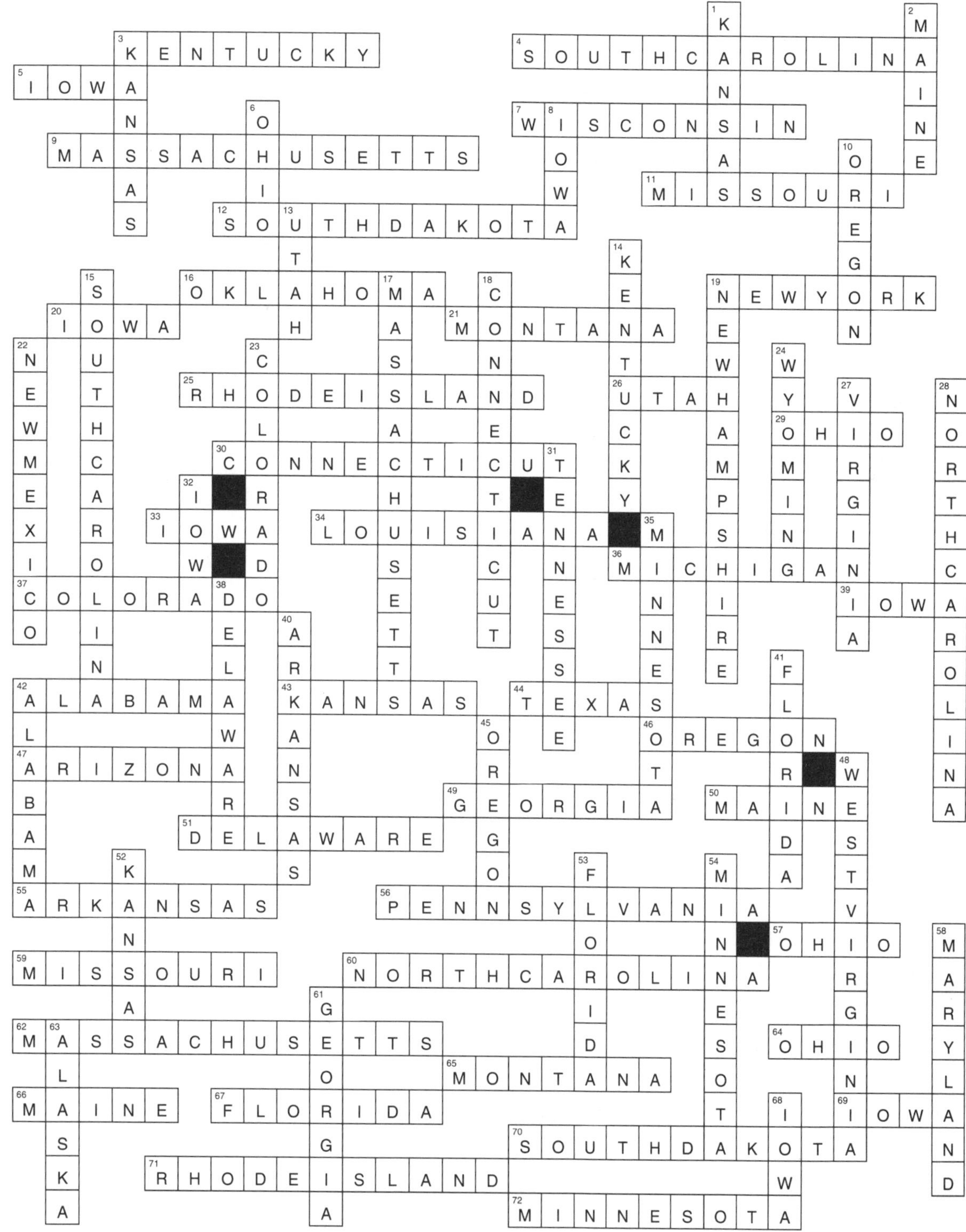

90. State Capitals

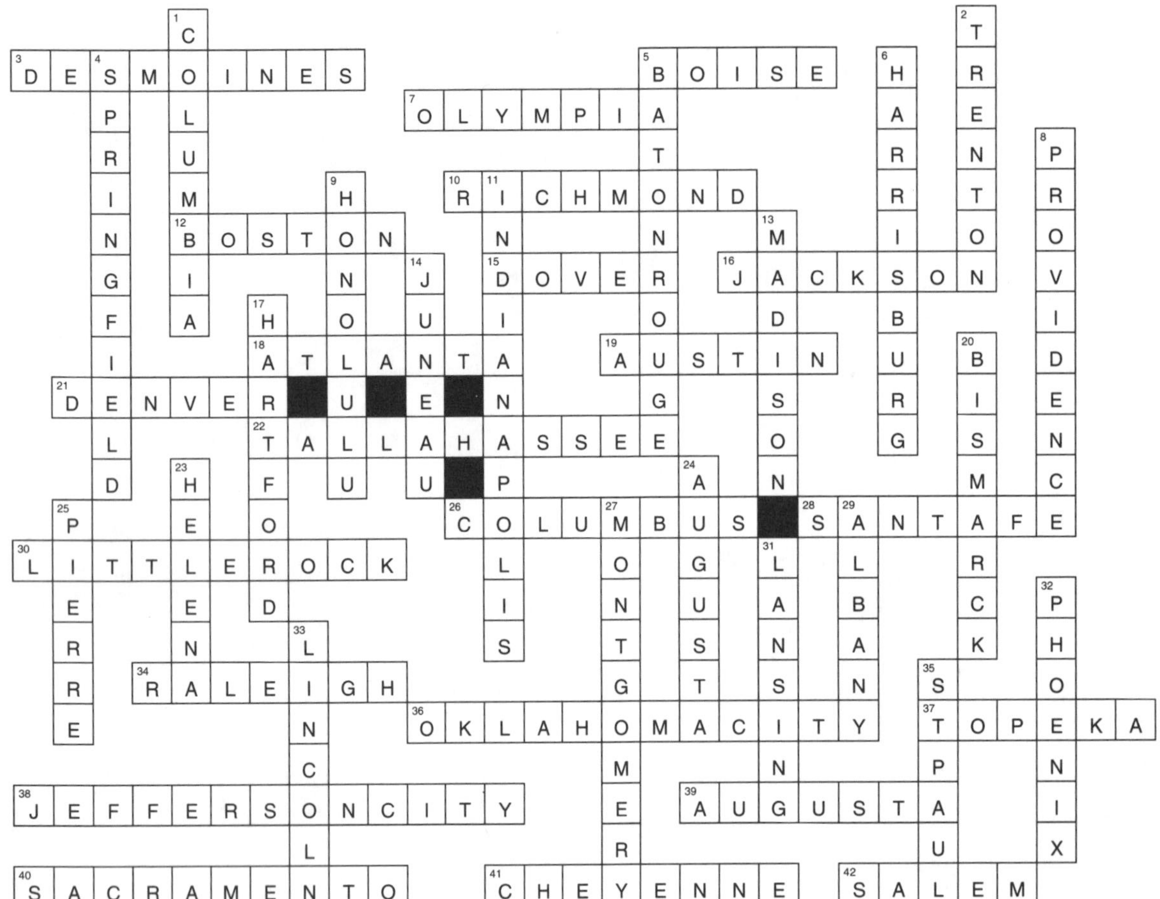

91. State Mottoes

Across

3. SOUTH DAKOTA
4. GEORGIA
7. OHIO
9. NEW HAMPSHIRE
12. TEXAS
14. MISSISSIPPI
17. OREGON
18. OHIO
20. TENNESSEE
22. ILLINOIS
23. OHIO
25. NEW YORK
28. IOWA
29. MINNESOTA
31. ALABAMA
33. OHIO
35. LOUISIANA
38. FLORIDA
40. CALIFORNIA
42. ARKANSAS
47. INDIANA
48. NEVADA
49. TEXAS
51. ALASKA
52. MASSACHUSETTS
53. NEW JERSEY
54. COLORADO

Down

1. IDAHO
2. IOWA
5. OREGON
6. UTAH
8. OHIO
10. MAINE
11. VERMONT
13. NORTH DAKOTA
14. MISSOURI
15. IOWA
16. PENNSYLVANIA
19. WEST VIRGINIA
21. VIRGINIA
24. MAINE
26. NEW MEXICO
27. MARYLAND
30. OKLAHOMA
32. ARIZONA
34. ILLINOIS
36. KANSAS
37. WASHINGTON
39. ALASKA
41. DELAWARE
43. KENTUCKY
44. UTAH
45. MAINE
46. HAWAII
50. IDAHO

92. State Birds

93. State Flowers

1. YUCCA
2. BLACKEYEDSUSAN
3. SAGEBRUSH
4. VIOLET
5. PEACHBLOSSOM
6. ROSE / RHODODENDRON
7. BLUECOLUMBINE
8. IRIS
9. ROSE
10. PEONY
11. SCARLETCARNATION
12. BLUEBONNET
13. FORGETMENOT
14. ROSE
15. CAMELLIA
16. YELLOWHIBISCUS
17. GOLDENPOPPY
18. SAGUAROBLOSSOM
19. SUNFLOWER
20. ORANGEBLOSSOM
21. WILDPRAIRIEROSE
22. FORGETMENOT
23. OREGONGRAPE
24. SEGOLILY
25. SYRINGA
26. GOLDENROD
27. VIOLET
28. CHEROKEEROSE
29. SYRINGA
30. DOGWOOD
31. BITTERROOT
32. REDCLOVER
33. YELLOWJESSAMINE
34. WILDROSE
35. IRIS
36. SYRINGA
37. ROSE
38. MAGNOLIA
39. GOLDENROD
40. MISTLETOE
41. LAUREL
42. IRIS
43. MAYFLOWER
44. YUCCA
45. PEONY
46. HAWTHORN
47. PASQUEFLOWER
48. PURPLELILAC

94. State Trees

1. MISSOURI
2. OREGON
3. IOWA
4. MONTANA
5. TEXAS
6. ALABAMA
7. ARIZONA
8. NEVADA
9. MISSISSIPPI
10. SOUTHCAROLINA
11. MAINE
12. CONNECTICUT
13. WASHINGTON
14. PENNSYLVANIA
15. ALASKA
16. RHODEISLAND
17. NEWHAMPSHIRE
18. UTAH
19. MASSACHUSETTS
20. KENTUCKY
21. COLORADO
22. DELAWARE
23. GEORGIA
24. TEXAS
25. ARKANSAS
26. HAWAII
27. UTAH
28. ILLINOIS
29. MARYLAND
30. IDAHO / INDIANA
31. FLORIDA
32. CALIFORNIA
33. VERMONT
34. OKLAHOMA
35. HAWAII
36. IOWA
37. LOUISIANA
38. IOWA
39. NEBRASKA
40. WESTVIRGINIA
41. IOWA
42. MICHIGAN
43. SOUTHDAKOTA

95. State Songs

1 KENTUCKY
2 UTAH
3 IDAHO
4 DELAWARE
5 WESTVIRGINIA
6 CONNECTICUT
7 VIRGINIA
7 VERMONT
8 KANSAS
9 OKLAHOMA
10 INDIANA
11 GEORGIA
12 IOWA
13 NEVADA
14 TENNESSEE
15 IOWA
16 RHODEISLAND
17 NEWYORK
18 MICHIGAN
19 IOWA
20 HAWAII
21 WISCONSIN
22 NORTHCAROLINA
23 IOWA
24 ARIZONA
25 MINNESOTA
26 SOUTHCAROLINA
27 HAWAII
28 OHIO
29 WYOMING
30 OHIO
31 MISSISSIPPI
32 NEBRASKA
33 ARKANSAS
34 NORTHDAKOTA
35 ALABAMA
36 OREGON
37 IOWA
38 ALASKA
39 CALIFORNIA
39 COLORADO
40 FLORIDA
41 MISSOURI
42 MONTANA
43 OHIO
44 MONTANA
45 TEXAS
45 TEXA
46 UTAH
47 MAINE
48 NEWMEXICO
49 INDIANA
50 NEWHAMPSHIRE

96. Largest Cities in the United States

2 MASSACHUSETTS
6 TENNESSEE
7 OREGON
8 MAINE
9 NEWMEXICO
11 ALASKA
13 MINNESOTA
17 UTAH
19 HAWAII
21 WYOMING
22 WISCONSIN
26 RHODEISLAND
27 MICHIGAN
29 PENNSYLVANIA
33 IOWA
35 VERMONT
36 ARIZONA
39 LOUISIANA
40 UTAH
42 IOWA
43 OHIO
45 CALIFORNIA
46 INDIANA
50 KANSAS
52 IOWA
53 KANSAS
54 COLORADO
55 ILLINOIS
56 NEVADA
57 DELAWARE

1 SOUTHDAKOTA
3 ARKANSAS
4 VERMONT
5 GEORGIA
6 TEXAS
10 WASHINGTON
12 ALABAMA
14 IDAHO
15 WISCONSIN
16 MISSISSIPPI
18 HAWAII
20 MONTANA
22 WESTVIRGINIA
23 NEBRASKA
24 MISSOURI
25 CONNECTICUT
28 NEVADA
30 SOUTHCAROLINA
31 FLORIDA
32 MAINE
34 OKLAHOMA
35 VIRGINIA
37 ILLINOIS
38 NEWHAMPSHIRE
41 KENTUCKY
44 MARYLAND
47 NEVADA
48 NEWYORK
49 MAINE
51 ALASKA

97. State Industries

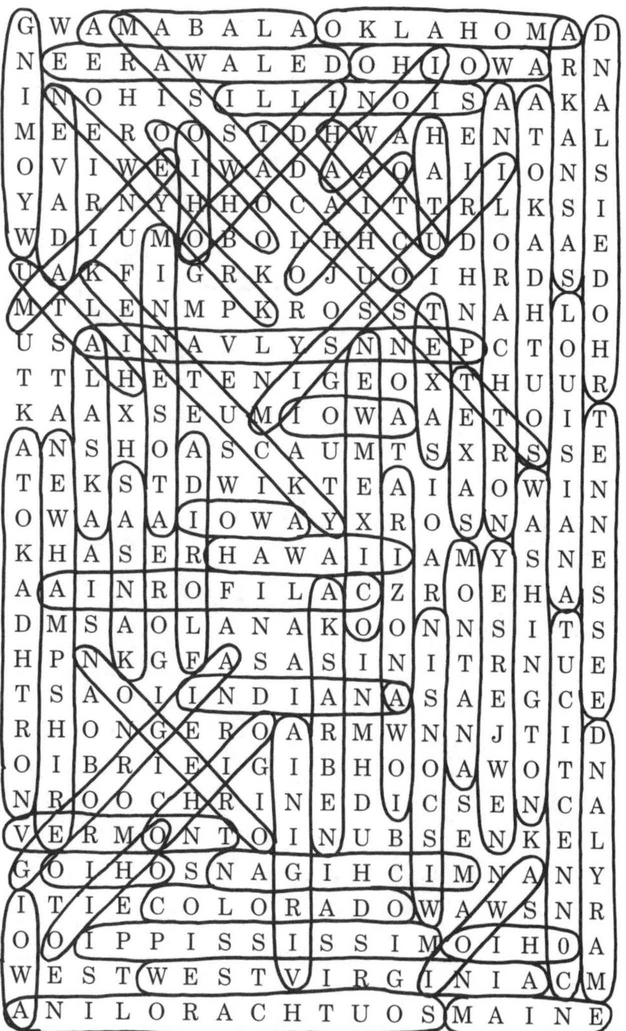

1. Alabama
2. Massachusetts
3. Pennsylvania
4. North Carolina
5. Idaho
6. Texas
7. Kentucky
8. Missouri
9. New Mexico
10. California
11. New Hampshire
12. Minnesota
13. Georgia
14. Nebraska
15. South Dakota
16. Indiana
17. Oregon
18. Arizona
19. Washington
20. Kansas
21. Wisconsin
22. Delaware
23. Ohio
24. Maine
25. Vermont
26. Illinois
27. New York
28. Michigan
29. Oklahoma
30. Colorado
31. Utah
32. Iowa
33. Nevada
34. Florida
35. North Dakota
36. Louisiana
37. Rhode Island
38. Alaska
39. Tennessee
40. Hawaii
41. Mississippi
42. Virginia
43. Connecticut
44. West Virginia
45. New Jersey
46. Maryland
47. South Carolina
48. Arkansas
49. Wyoming
50. Montana

98. State Size

```
R C E G W I A N I L O R A C H T R O N S B E R G E
A A T E N N E S S E E E O H A D I S I T O U A N S
C F L I D N A L S I E D O H R I L O N T N O P I O
S T N A G I H C I M V A A E A I O U U E E D G M U
H J E K B L N D O R S T X W A U M T O S W E T O T
O I B B E A G E O R G I A G I K A H C U J Y N Y H
L O R P I R M L T A F H A L A B R C I H E C O W D
A D A V E N E A I K E N T U C K Y A X C R O M R A
A L S O U T K W I S C O U S A H L R E A S I R E K
N O K S A S N A K A N S C O L O A O M S E N E R O
E T A L A B A R H S O U I O W A N L W S Y O V I T
W A S L I N G E A S A R T E X S D I E A Z R W O A
H A A R I Z O N A L A X C A A L I N N M U T I A T
A D I R O L F L O O H I E S O U T A M I N H S E O
M S Y R I O W A I O W E N T E N I O H S E D C A B
P E I N N Z I H A W A A N O R S T K E S I A O I R
S R C O I H O H I O K A O H I O W A T I S K N N E
H A R R N O R N E R A S C U K A N M E S T O S I R
I O W A D I M C A L I F O R N I A N I S M T I G O
R I S S I S L O H I O L O U I I O W A I R A N R S
E A R O A T E L N O N E B R N E W Y S P E N N I S
I O W A N H I O I T E O F E R S T S O P I U T V I
B A U T A H A R R I A B G I R W O H I I O W A T U
N O R T H D A A C A L N I E S U G E O R G I A S T
S O U T H C A D I D A H A I R V I R G I N I A E O
E M I N N E S O T A I J O I N O T G N I H S A W Z
O R E G A I N A V L Y S N N E P O K L A H O M A E
```

1. Rhode Island
2. Delaware
3. Connecticut
4. Hawaii
5. New Jersey
6. Massachusetts
7. New Hampshire
8. Vermont
9. Maryland
10. West Virginia
11. South Carolina
12. Maine
13. Indiana
14. Kentucky
15. Virginia
16. Ohio
17. Tennessee
18. Pennsylvania
19. Mississippi
20. Louisiana
21. New York
22. Alabama
23. North Carolina
24. Arkansas
25. Wisconsin
26. Iowa
27. Illinois
28. Michigan
29. Florida
30. Georgia
31. Washington
32. Missouri
33. Oklahoma
34. North Dakota
35. South Dakota
36. Nebraska
37. Kansas
38. Idaho
39. Minnesota
40. Utah
41. Oregon
42. Wyoming
43. Colorado
44. Nevada
45. Arizona
46. New Mexico
47. Montana
48. California
49. Texas
50. Alaska

99. State Population Density

4. CALIFORNIA
5. COLORADO
8. ARIZONA
10. FLORIDA
11. KANSAS
12. ALABAMA
14. OHIO
15. SOUTHCAROLINA
18. MAINE
19. HAWAII
21. NORTHCAROLINA
23. MISSISSIPPI
28. NEVADA
29. ALASKA
30. TEXAS
31. HAWAII
32. NEWJERSEY
36. LOUISIANA
37. UTAH
38. KENTUCKY
39. LOUISIANA
40. TENNESSEE
42. SOUTHDAKOTA
44. TEXAS
45. VIRGINIA
46. IOWA
48. RHODEISLAND
49. ILLINOIS

1. FLORIDA
2. MARYLAND
3. IOWA
4. COLORADO
6. MISSOURI
7. WASHINGTON
9. WESTVIRGINIA
13. MONTANA
16. NEWHAMPSHIRE
17. MINNESOTA
18. MICHIGAN
20. NEWMEXICO
22. ARKANSAS
24. IDAHO
25. IOWA
26. PENNSYLVANIA
27. MASSACHUSETTS
33. WISCONSIN
34. ALABAMA
35. IOWA
41. OREGON
43. HAWAII
47. OHIO

100. State Date of Entry into the Union

1 HAWAII
2 IOWA
3 CONNECTICUT
4 OKLAHOMA
5 MAINE
6 NEW MEXICO
7 MISSISSIPPI
8 FLORIDA
9 ILLINOIS
10 OHIO
11 ALASKA
12 MISSOURI
13 NEW JERSEY
14 WEST VIRGINIA
15 OREGON
16 TEXAS
17 TEXAS
18 TENNESSEE
19 MONTANA
20 WYOMING
21 PENNSYLVANIA
22 IDAHO
23 COLORADO
24 MICHIGAN
25 MINNESOTA
26 DELAWARE
27 KENTUCKY
28 LOUISIANA
29 MARYLAND
30 CALIFORNIA
31 KANSAS
32 UTAH
33 IOWA
34 ALASKA
35 IOWA
36 RHODE ISLAND
37 IDAHO
38 WISCONSIN
39 ARKANSAS / ARIZONA
40 KANSAS
41 ALABAMA
42 UTAH
43 UTAH
44 INDIANA
45 WASHINGTON
46 OHIO
47 COLORADO
48 MASSACHUSETTS
49 TEXAS

101. State Order of Entry into the Union

1. IOWA
2. MONTANA
3. COLORADO; CONNECTICUT
4. WASHINGTON
5. IOWA
6. IDAHO
7. SOUTHDAKOTA
8. LOUISIANA
9. MASSACHUSETTS
10. TEXAS
11. NEWMEXICO
12. TEXAS
13. INDIANA
14. ILLINOIS
15. PENNSYLVANIA
16. VIRGINIA
17. WESTVIRGINIA
18. NEWHAMPSHIRE
19. ALASKA
20. UTAH
21. MISSISSIPPI
22. OKLAHOMA
23. DELAWARE
24. RHODEISLAND
25. UTAH
26. MISSOURI
27. ARKANSAS
28. NEWJERSEY
29. UTAH
30. GEORGIA
31. HAWAII
32. NORTHCAROLINA
33. ARIZONA
34. IOWA
35. MARYLAND
36. NEBRASKA
37. CALIFORNIA
38. ALABAMA
39. MAINE; MAINE
40. IDAHO
41. NEVADA
42. FLORIDA
43. SOUTHCAROLINA
44. OHIO
45. OREGON
46. NEWYORK
47. VERMONT
48. MAINE
49. IOWA
50. NORTHDAKOTA
51. OHIO
52. KANSAS
53. IOWA
54. MAINE
55. TENNESSEE
56. WYOMING

102. Famous Sons and Daughters—I

1. CALI**F**ORNIA
2. ALAB**A**MA
3. NEWHA**M**PSHIRE
4. COL**O**RADO
5. MASSACH**U**SETTS
6. KAN**S**AS

7. LOUI**S**IANA
8. GE**O**RGIA
9. ILLI**N**OIS
10. MISSI**S**SIPPI

11. ID**A**HO
12. MIN**N**ESOTA
13. SOUTH**D**AKOTA

14. FLORI**D**A
15. ARK**A**NSAS
16. KENT**U**CKY
17. MICHI**G**AN
18. MASSAC**H**USETTS
19. CONNEC**T**ICUT
20. MINN**E**SOTA
21. GEO**R**GIA
22. LOUI**S**IANA

103. Famous Sons and Daughters—II

1. CALI**F**ORNIA
2. MARYL**A**ND
3. ALABA**M**A
4. I**O**WA
5. KENT**U**CKY
6. TENNE**S**SEE
7. TENNE**S**SEE
8. ARIZ**O**NA
9. MAI**N**E
10. MISSI**S**SIPPI
11. DEL**A**WARE
12. MIN**N**ESOTA
13. IN**D**IANA
14. RHO**D**EISLAND
15. NEBR**A**SKA
16. MISSO**U**RI
17. VIR**G**INIA
18. WAS**H**INGTON
19. MON**T**ANA
20. CONN**E**CTICUT
21. GEO**R**GIA
22. MIS**S**OURI

104. Famous Sons and Daughters—III

1. **F**LORIDA
2. NORTHC**A**ROLINA
3. VER**M**ONT
4. **O**HIO
5. MASSACH**U**SETTS
6. PENN**S**YLVANIA
7. TEXA**S**
8. I**O**WA
9. ILLI**N**OIS
10. WI**S**CONSIN
11. SOUTHC**A**ROLINA
12. MAI**N**E
13. RHO**D**EISLAND
14. IN**D**IANA
15. AL**A**BAMA
16. MISSO**U**RI
17. WESTVIR**G**INIA
18. NORT**H**DAKOTA
19. CONNEC**T**ICUT
20. NEWM**E**XICO
21. MA**R**YLAND
22. MIS**S**ISSIPPI

105. Famous Sons and Daughters—IV

1. CALI**F**ORNIA
2. MASS**A**CHUSETTS
3. NEW**M**EXICO
4. NEWY**O**RK
5. MISSO**U**RI
6. TENNE**S**SEE
7. MINNE**S**OTA
8. OHI**O**
9. INDIA**N**A
10. NEBRA**S**KA
11. M**A**RYLAND
12. ILLI**N**OIS
13. NORTH**D**AKOTA
14. RHO**D**EISLAND
15. UT**A**H
16. KENT**U**CKY
17. WESTVIR**G**INIA
18. OKLA**H**OMA
19. NOR**T**HCAROLINA
20. NEWJ**E**RSEY
21. NORTHCA**R**OLINA
22. PENN**S**YLVANIA

106. Famous Sons and Daughters—V

1. F L O R I D A
2. V I R G I N I A
3. W Y O M I N G
4. N E W Y O R K
5. L O U I S I A N A
6. N E W J E R S E Y
7. N E W H A M P S H I R E
8. O H I O
9. C O N N E C T I C U T
10. P E N N S Y L V A N I A
11. O K L A H O M A
12. I L L I N O I S
13. I N D I A N A
14. S O U T H D A K O T A
15. T E X A S
16. U T A H
17. V I R G I N I A
18. O H I O
19. M I N N E S O T A
20. N E W Y O R K
21. V E R M O N T
22. N E B R A S K A

Down (bold letters): **FAMOUS SONS AND DAUGHTERS**

107. Famous Sons and Daughters—VI

1. CALI**F**ORNIA
2. ARK**A**NSAS
3. NEWHA**M**PSHIRE
4. I**O**WA
5. KENT**U**CKY
6. ALA**S**KA
7. KAN**S**AS
8. **O**HIO
9. MAI**N**E
10. MISSI**S**SIPPI
11. DEL**A**WARE
12. ARIZO**N**A
13. I**D**AHO
14. FLORI**D**A
15. NEV**A**DA
16. MISSO**U**RI
17. GEOR**G**IA
18. MIC**H**IGAN
19. MON**T**ANA
20. OR**E**GON
21. COLO**R**ADO
22. ALA**S**KA

108. State Historical Highlights—I

1. NEW HAMP**S**HIRE
2. MON**T**ANA
3. HAW**A**II
4. CONNEC**T**ICUT
5. T**E**XAS
6. O**H**IO
7. ILL**I**NOIS
8. MISSI**S**SIPPI
9. U**T**AH
10. NEWY**O**RK
11. GEO**R**GIA
12. VIRG**I**NIA
13. KENTU**C**KY
14. ALAB**A**MA
15. SOUTHCARO**L**INA
16. MASSAC**H**USETTS
17. CALI**I**FORNIA
18. VIR**G**INIA
19. WAS**H**INGTON
20. MARY**L**AND
21. AR**I**ZONA
22. WESTVIR**G**INIA
23. SOUT**H**DAKOTA
24. VERMON**T**
25. NEWJER**S**EY

109. State Historical Highlights—II

1. MI**S**SOURI
2. VERMON**T**
3. M**A**RYLAND
4. KEN**T**UCKY
5. NEWM**E**XICO
6. MASSAC**H**USETTS
7. IND**I**ANA
8. NEWHAMP**S**HIRE
9. CONNEC**T**ICUT
10. WY**O**MING
11. NEWYO**R**K
12. ILL**I**NOIS
13. SOUTH**C**AROLINA
14. ALAB**A**MA
15. F**L**ORIDA
16. UTA**H**
17. AR**I**ZONA
18. VIR**G**INIA
19. SOUT**H**DAKOTA
20. CO**L**ORADO
21. LOU**I**SIANA
22. **G**EORGIA
23. O**H**IO
24. **T**EXAS
25. MISSI**S**SIPPI

110. State Historical Highlights—III

1. N E W J E R **S** E Y
2. M O N **T** A N A
3. A R K **A** N S A S
4. K E N **T** U C K Y
5. N **E** W Y O R K

6. S O U T **H** D A K O T A
7. O H **I** O
8. T E N N E **S** S E E
9. C O N N E C **T** I C U T
10. A R I Z **O** N A
11. C O L O **R** A D O
12. C A L **I** F O R N I A
13. M A S S A **C** H U S E T T S
14. A L **A** B A M A
15. F **L** O R I D A

16. M A S S A C **H** U S E T T S
17. I N D **I** A N A
18. V I R **G** I N I A
19. O **H** I O
20. C O **L** O R A D O
21. L O U I S **I** A N A
22. G E O R **G** I A
23. I D A **H** O
24. K E N **T** U C K Y
25. L O U I **S** I A N A

111. State Historical Highlights—IV

1. KANSAS
2. CONNECTICUT
3. MASSACHUSETTS
4. TENNESSEE
5. NEW JERSEY
6. MASSACHUSETTS
7. LOUISIANA
8. ALASKA
9. KENTUCKY
10. NEW YORK
11. NEBRASKA
12. FLORIDA
13. CONNECTICUT
14. IDAHO
15. MARYLAND
16. OHIO
17. CALIFORNIA
18. GEORGIA
19. MASSACHUSETTS
20. ALABAMA
21. ILLINOIS
22. GEORGIA
23. IDAHO
24. CONNECTICUT
25. PENNSYLVANIA

STATE HISTORICAL HIGHLIGHTS

112. State Historical Highlights—V

1. ALA**S**KA
2. **T**EXAS
3. AL**A**BAMA
4. U**T**AH
5. NEWJ**E**RSEY
6. MASSAC**H**USETTS
7. CAL**I**FORNIA
8. PENN**S**YLVANIA
9. KEN**T**UCKY
10. NEWY**O**RK
11. NEWYO**R**K
12. ILL**I**NOIS
13. WIS**C**ONSIN
14. NEV**A**DA
15. A**L**ABAMA
16. SOUT**H**DAKOTA
17. CAL**I**FORNIA
18. WASHIN**G**TON
19. O**H**IO
20. MARY**L**AND
21. VIRG**I**NIA
22. GEOR**G**IA
23. NEW**H**AMPSHIRE
24. **T**ENNESSEE
25. KAN**S**AS

113. State Historical Highlights—VI

1. MISSI**S**SIPPI
2. SOU**T**HCAROLINA
3. AL**A**SKA
4. MON**T**ANA
5. MINN**E**SOTA

6. MIC**H**IGAN
7. WYOM**I**NG
8. MIS**S**OURI
9. NOR**T**HCAROLINA
10. ARIZ**O**NA
11. FLO**R**IDA
12. MA**I**NE
13. WIS**C**ONSIN
14. NEBR**A**SKA
15. IL**L**INOIS

16. MASSAC**H**USETTS
17. M**I**SSOURI
18. VIR**G**INIA
19. NORT**H**CAROLINA
20. MARY**L**AND
21. VIRG**I**NIA
22. ORE**G**ON
23. MIC**H**IGAN
24. NOR**T**HDAKOTA
25. PENN**S**YLVANIA

114. State Oddities and Specialties—I

1. NEBRA**S**KA
2. NOR**T**HCAROLINA
3. ARK**A**NSAS
4. KEN**T**UCKY
5. MINN**E**SOTA

6. FL**O**RIDA
7. IN**D**IANA
8. I**D**AHO
9. MA**I**NE
10. KEN**T**UCKY
11. ILL**I**NOIS
12. CONN**E**CTICUT
13. KAN**S**AS

14. ALAB**A**MA
15. ILLI**N**OIS
16. NEVA**D**A

17. ALA**S**KA
18. NEWHAM**P**SHIRE
19. N**E**VADA
20. CONNE**C**TICUT
21. LOU**I**SIANA
22. ID**A**HO
23. MARY**L**AND
24. KEN**T**UCKY
25. CAL**I**FORNIA
26. NEWJ**E**RSEY
27. MISSISSIPPI

115. State Oddities and Specialties—II

1. KANSAS
2. KENTUCKY
3. DELAWARE
4. CONNECTICUT
5. MINNESOTA
6. IOWA
7. NEVADA
8. RHODEISLAND
9. LOUISIANA
10. WASHINGTON
11. ARIZONA
12. GEORGIA
13. NEBRASKA
14. HAWAII
15. ARKANSAS
16. IDAHO
17. PENNSYLVANIA
18. MISSISSIPPI
19. NEWJERSEY
20. MASSACHUSETTS
21. ILLINOIS
22. ALABAMA
23. MARYLAND
24. UTAH
25. HAWAII
26. NEWMEXICO
27. MISSISSIPPI

116. State Oddities and Specialties—III

1. ALA**S**KA
2. NOR**T**HCAROLINA
3. MICHIG**A**N
4. **T**EXAS
5. NEWM**E**XICO
6. GE**O**RGIA
7. COLORA**D**O
8. RHO**D**EISLAND
9. ILL**I**NOIS
10. VERMON**T**
11. CAL**I**FORNIA
12. NEWJ**E**RSEY
13. TENNE**S**SEE
14. H**A**WAII
15. WASHI**N**GTON
16. RHO**D**EISLAND
17. MIS**S**OURI
18. MISSISSI**P**PI
19. NEWJ**E**RSEY
20. MASSA**C**HUSETTS
21. MA**I**NE
22. DEL**A**WARE
23. CO**L**ORADO
24. VERMON**T**
25. **I**OWA
26. NEWJ**E**RSEY
27. KAN**S**AS

117. State Oddities and Specialties—IV

1. MASSACHU**S**ETTS
2. **T**EXAS
3. MARYL**A**ND
4. CONNEC**T**ICUT
5. TENN**E**SSEE
6. GE**O**RGIA
7. NEVA**D**A
8. SOUTH**D**AKOTA
9. MA**I**NE
10. **T**EXAS
11. CAL**I**FORNIA
12. NEWM**E**XICO
13. WI**S**CONSIN
14. NORTHC**A**ROLINA
15. MAI**N**E
16. NEVA**D**A
17. PENN**S**YLVANIA
18. NEWHAM**P**SHIRE
19. NEWJ**E**RSEY
20. NORTH**C**AROLINA
21. AR**I**ZONA
22. MARYL**A**ND
23. DE**L**AWARE
24. WASHING**T**ON
25. MICH**I**GAN
26. OR**E**GON
27. LOUI**S**IANA

118. State Oddities and Specialties—V

1. MIS**S**OURI
2. WES**T**VIRGINIA
3. ARK**A**NSAS
4. **T**EXAS
5. TENN**E**SSEE
6. WY**O**MING
7. NORTH**D**AKOTA
8. NEVA**D**A
9. OH**I**O
10. VERMON**T**
11. CAL**I**FORNIA
12. TENN**E**SSEE
13. PENN**S**YLVANIA
14. NORTHC**A**ROLINA
15. ILLI**N**OIS
16. SOUTH**D**AKOTA
17. ALA**S**KA
18. MISSISSI**P**PI
19. CONN**E**CTICUT
20. SOUTH**C**AROLINA
21. WESTV**I**RGINIA
22. AL**A**BAMA
23. PENNSY**L**VANIA
24. U**T**AH
25. OH**I**O
26. OR**E**GON
27. MISSIS**S**IPPI

119. State Oddities and Specialties—VI

1. PENNSYLVANIA
2. TENNESSEE
3. HAWAII
4. VERMONT
5. GEORGIA
6. WYOMING
7. FLORIDA
8. RHODEISLAND
9. WYOMING
10. NORTHCAROLINA
11. MAINE
12. NEWYORK
13. PENNSYLVANIA
14. NORTHCAROLINA
15. MARYLAND
16. SOUTHDAKOTA
17. ALASKA
18. MISSISSIPPI
19. NEWYORK
20. MASSACHUSETTS
21. VIRGINIA
22. IOWA
23. PENNSYLVANIA
24. WESTVIRGINIA
25. OHIO
26. OREGON
27. PENNSYLVANIA

120. State Places to Visit—I

1. LOUI**S**IANA
2. MON**T**ANA
3. NORTHC**A**ROLINA
4. CONNEC**T**ICUT
5. TENN**E**SSEE
6. MISSISSI**P**PI
7. MARY**L**AND
8. NEBR**A**SKA
9. NORTH**C**AROLINA
10. NEWM**E**XICO
11. PENN**S**YLVANIA
12. **T**EXAS
13. COL**O**RADO
14. NE**V**ADA
15. MICH**I**GAN
16. ALA**S**KA
17. FLOR**I**DA
18. U**T**AH

121. State Places to Visit—II

1 P E N N **S** Y L V A N I A
2 N O R **T** H D A K O T A
3 H A W **A** I I
4 W A S H I N G **T** O N
5 O R **E** G O N

6 N E W H A M **P** S H I R E
7 O K **L** A H O M A
8 A L **A** B A M A
9 S O U T H **C** A R O L I N A
10 T E N N **E** S S E E
11 M I S **S** O U R I

12 C O N N E C **T** I C U T
13 W Y **O** M I N G

14 **V** I R G I N I A
15 C A L **I** F O R N I A
16 T E N N E **S** S E E
17 W A S H **I** N G T O N
18 K E N **T** U C K Y

122. State Places to Visit—III

1. ARKAN**S**AS
2. MASSACHUSE**T**TS
3. C**A**LIFORNIA
4. KEN**T**UCKY
5. N**E**WYORK
6. MISSISSIP**P**I
7. F**L**ORIDA
8. ID**A**HO
9. **C**ALIFORNIA
10. G**E**ORGIA
11. KAN**S**AS
12. U**T**AH
13. ARIZ**O**NA
14. **V**IRGINIA
15. IND**I**ANA
16. ARKAN**S**AS
17. AR**I**ZONA
18. CONNEC**T**ICUT

123. State Places to Visit—IV

1. K A N **S** A S
2. M O N **T** A N A
3. A L **A** B A M A
4. N O R **T** H C A R O L I N A
5. T E N N **E** S S E E
6. M I S S I S S I **P** P I
7. C O **L** O R A D O
8. A L **A** S K A
9. K E N T U **C** K Y
10. N E W M **E** X I C O
11. A R K A N **S** A S
12. S O U **T** H D A K O T A
13. A R I Z **O** N A
14. N E **V** A D A
15. H A W A **I** I
16. R H O D E I **S** L A N D
17. C A L **I** F O R N I A
18. **T** E X A S

124. State Places to Visit—V

1. MINNE**S**OTA
2. SOU**T**HCAROLINA
3. GEORGI**A**
4. **T**EXAS
5. NEWJ**E**RSEY
6. **P**ENNSYLVANIA
7. CA**L**IFORNIA
8. ID**A**HO
9. MI**C**HIGAN
10. N**E**WYORK
11. LOUI**S**IANA
12. MINNESO**T**A
13. FL**O**RIDA
14. **V**ERMONT
15. IND**I**ANA
16. MAS**S**ACHUSETTS
17. ILL**I**NOIS
18. SOU**T**HDAKOTA

125. State Places to Visit—VI

1. MIS**S**OURI
2. KEN**T**UCKY
3. NEBR**A**SKA
4. **T**EXAS
5. N**E**WYORK
6. NEWHAM**P**SHIRE
7. CO**L**ORADO
8. MARYL**A**ND
9. MASSA**C**HUSETTS
10. G**E**ORGIA
11. NEWJER**S**EY
12. MON**T**ANA
13. CALIF**O**RNIA
14. PENNSYL**V**ANIA
15. CAL**I**FORNIA
16. MIS**S**OURI
17. FLOR**I**DA
18. MASSACHUSET**T**S

126. State Colleges and Universities—I

1. SOUTH**C**AROLINA
2. NEWY**O**RK
3. MARY**L**AND
4. PENNSY**L**VANIA
5. T**E**XAS
6. VIR**G**INIA
7. TENN**E**SSEE
8. KAN**S**AS

9. INDI**A**NA
10. ILLI**N**OIS
11. RHO**D**EISLAND

12. LO**U**ISIANA
13. MAI**N**E
14. INDI**I**ANA
15. PENNSYL**V**ANIA
16. TENN**E**SSEE
17. NORTHCA**R**OLINA
18. NEWHAMP**S**HIRE
19. CAL**I**FORNIA
20. CONNEC**T**ICUT
21. OH**I**O
22. T**E**XAS
23. LOUI**S**IANA

127. State Colleges and Universities—II

1. N O R T H **C** A R O L I N A
2. N E W Y **O** R K
3. M A R Y **L** A N D
4. A **L** A B A M A
5. N E W J **E** R S E Y
6. G E O R **G** I A
7. N **E** W Y O R K
8. M A **S** S A C H U S E T T S
9. N O R T H C **A** R O L I N A
10. V I R G I **N** I A
11. I N **D** I A N A
12. M A S S A C H **U** S E T T S
13. **N** E W Y O R K
14. V I R G **I** N I A
15. P E N N S Y L **V** A N I A
16. N E W J **E** R S E Y
17. N E W Y O **R** K
18. T E N N E **S** S E E
19. **I** O W A
20. K E N **T** U C K Y
21. O H **I** O
22. N **E** W Y O R K
23. N E W J E R **S** E Y

128. State Wordsearch

```
W A S M A I N N E W H A M P S H I R E A A T
I R S O I D A H O O S A R A W O I T I L T E
S A M C O N N E C T I C U T X H Y N U A O N
C N I I D F N H L N P A N O Z I R A V B K N
W I C X A W E E E Q O K L A H O M A Y A A E
E L H E R D S A S A X E T N F O R D K M D I
S O I M O F E G N O T G N I H S A W C A H N
T R G W L I K L A S T O L R I B I R U A T D
V A A E O S R M A S S A C H U S E T T S R I
I C N N C E O R D W C H A C C O O N N E O A
R H K A N R Y S A S A L A O K U T E E A N N
G T E X E M W I S T I R N E B T E W K A D A
I R H G M O E T U T A S E X Y H A J A M N E
N O O H A I N I G R I V I R G C O E J W A S
I N E V A D S O U N G S A S N A K R A L L G
A I N A V L Y S N N E P L T T R I S O U S T
A L A S S O U T I D E H A O H O I E A S I R
M I S S I I X M A S S V K A U L A Y U R E E
H A W A I I O W I S S A A L A I O W U A D E
R K N E V Y A N O R D I S D O N S O D S O S
A S I A W A I I I H A W P E A A S I S L H S
C A L L T E G E T L O U I P S S R H A C R E
I R F A R N R U T A L K E N I O K L A N E N
O B I S O U O R E G O I A M L M A R Y L A N
K E N K I S E M A I N K A F L O R I S A E E
O N A A L A G D N A L Y R A M V E R M O N T
```

1. Alabama
2. Alaska
3. Arizona
4. Arkansas
5. California
6. Colorado
7. Connecticut
8. Delaware
9. Florida
10. Georgia
11. Hawaii
12. Idaho
13. Illinois
14. Indiana
15. Iowa
16. Kansas
17. Kentucky
18. Louisiana
19. Maine
20. Maryland
21. Massachusetts
22. Michigan
23. Minnesota
24. Mississippi
25. Missouri
26. Montana
27. Nebraska
28. Nevada
29. New Hampshire
30. New Jersey
31. New Mexico
32. New York
33. North Carolina
34. North Dakota
35. Ohio
36. Oklahoma
37. Oregon
38. Pennsylvania
39. Rhode Island
40. South Carolina
41. South Dakota
42. Tennessee
43. Texas
44. Utah
45. Vermont
46. Virginia
47. Washington
48. West Virginia
49. Wisconsin
50. Wyoming

129. State Capital Wordsearch

```
E D M A R H A R R I S B U R G R I C H M E
B E L L I V H S A N N O S K C A J O M H C
K N E W B I S M A R C K N A S H U O H A N
S V X H S U B M U L O C E F D E N V E R E
C E Y O J I T O R J E K A K A T E O L T D
R O T N E M A R C A S M D C G U A L E F I
I K I O S P L H E X I N E O H P U S N O V
J L C L I S L A L L O N M R V T S I O R O
O A N U L L A L A B B E T E N E P L T D R
M H O L O L H S A N R L A L A Y R O S A P
P O S U P Y A E I Y C I T T A T I P E I C
A M R R A S S T L N I N L T O I N A L P O
R A E L N O S S R E O A A I I C G N R M L
E C F U N U E T O R N T N L X N F A A Y U
U I F R A K E P O T Y A S Z R O I I H L M
I T E R A S K A A S E N I O M S E D C O B
Z Y J S O N R U S U M O N I B R L N O Y I
D D I E L U K L A N G O G I X A D I N P A
N N M F E I F F O R D U P N A C A A C O E
O O B A T O N R O U G E S O N E B R O E N
M M O T A N A C I R E S A T I L L E R S N
H H O N O L U L O S T A R N A D E R D I E
C C R A S H G I E L A R I E T E E S I T Y
I I A S H A R R I S N I O R C I T Y S I E
R E I L E P T N O M U X P T P O M M E R H
A S A L T L A K E C I T Y N O S I D A M C
```

Montgomery	Alabama	Baton Rouge	Louisiana	Columbus	Ohio
Juneau	Alaska	Augusta	Maine	Oklahoma City	Oklahoma
Phoenix	Arizona	Annapolis	Maryland	Salem	Oregon
Little Rock	Arkansas	Boston	Massachusetts	Harrisburg	Pennsylvania
Sacramento	California	Lansing	Michigan	Providence	Rhode Island
Denver	Colorado	St. Paul	Minnesota	Columbia	South Carolina
Hartford	Connecticut	Jackson	Mississippi	Pierre	South Dakota
Dover	Delaware	Jefferson City	Missouri	Nashville	Tennessee
Tallahassee	Florida	Helena	Montana	Austin	Texas
Atlanta	Georgia	Lincoln	Nebraska	Salt Lake City	Utah
Honolulu	Hawaii	Carson City	Nevada	Montpelier	Vermont
Boise	Idaho	Concord	New Hampshire	Richmond	Virginia
Springfield	Illinois	Trenton	New Jersey	Olympia	Washington
Indianapolis	Indiana	Santa Fe	New Mexico	Charleston	West Virginia
Des Moines	Iowa	Albany	New York	Madison	Wisconsin
Topeka	Kansas	Raleigh	North Carolina	Cheyenne	Wyoming
Frankfort	Kentucky	Bismarck	North Dakota		

130. State Silhouettes

1. Maryland
2. Rhode Island
3. West Virginia
4. Utah
5. Nevada
6. Massachusetts
7. Maine
8. Hawaii
9. Indiana
10. Virginia
11. Pennsylvania
12. Iowa
13. New York
14. Illinois
15. New Hampshire
16. Colorado
17. South Carolina
18. Washington
19. Kansas
20. Michigan
21. Idaho
22. New Mexico
23. Connecticut
24. Mississippi
25. Nebraska
26. Minnesota
27. New Jersey
28. Alaska
29. Arkansas
30. Georgia
31. Wisconsin
32. Kentucky
33. Tennessee
34. Ohio
35. Delaware
36. Oklahoma
37. Oregon
38. Alabama
39. Florida
40. Vermont
41. Texas
42. Montana
43. South Dakota
44. North Dakota
45. Arizona
46. Missouri
47. Wyoming
48. North Carolina
49. California
50. Louisiana

131. State Flags

1. Texas
2. Wyoming
3. North Dakota
4. Rhode Island
5. Virginia
6. Oklahoma
7. Florida
8. Louisiana
9. Missouri
10. Tennessee
11. Delaware
12. Maine
13. Iowa
14. New Mexico
15. Kansas
16. Washington
17. Connecticut
18. Mississippi
19. Arkansas
20. North Carolina
21. Indiana
22. Maryland
23. Vermont
24. Georgia
25. Nevada
26. Pennsylvania
27. South Carolina
28. Oregon
29. New York
30. West Virginia
31. Nebraska
32. Kentucky
33. South Dakota
34. Michigan
35. New Hampshire
36. Idaho
37. Utah
38. Colorado
39. Montana
40. Hawaii
41. Ohio
42. Arizona
43. Minnesota
44. Illinois
45. Alabama
46. Wisconsin
47. Alaska
48. California
49. Massachusetts
50. New Jersey